# Cadbury's
## NINTH BOOK OF
# CHILDREN'S POETRY

RED FOX

A Red Fox Book
Published by Random Century Children's Books
20 Vauxhall Bridge Road, London SW1V 2SA

A division of the Random Century Group
London Melbourne Sydney Auckland
Johannesburg and agencies throughout the world

First published by Red Fox 1991
© National Exhibition of Children's Art 1991

Set in Garamond
Typeset by JH Graphics Limited, Reading

Printed and bound in Great Britain
by Cox & Wyman Ltd, Reading

ISBN 0 09 983450 2

# Contents

# Publisher's note

The poems in this book were chosen by a panel of judges which included poets, teachers and educationalists, from over 40,000 entries for Cadbury's 1991/92 National Exhibition of Children's Art. This year is the ninth in which there has been a Poetry section and the final judges – Jennifer Curry, Chairman of the Advisory Panel, anthologist and author; Wes Magee, poet and author; Gareth Owen, poet, novelist and playwright; and Michael Rosen, children's author, poet and anthologist – were delighted at the great variety of material. James Allen's Girls' School won the Cadbury's Creative School of the Year award, and they chose as outstanding the work of Catherine Wilkinson, whose poems appear on pages 66 and 112.

Twenty other children have had their work awarded silver medals by the judges. Their poems appear on pages 18, 35, 36, 49, 50, 59, 62, 72, 79, 85, 96, 111, 112, 115, 118, 130, 142, 145, 146, 173. Michael Davies and Rachel Muers were chosen for the Most Promising Individual Award. Their poems appear on pages 112 and 130. Debenham High School won the Cadbury's Gold Medal Award for Schools.

The Poems have been placed into chapters to give the reader the opportunity to compare the ideas of children from as young as four to mature seventeen year olds on just about every conceivable subject. All the illustrations are taken from entries to the Art & Design section of this year's Exhibition, and they complement the poems in an unusual and pleasing way.

We are very happy to be publishing such an interesting and original book and would like to thank all the writers and artists for their superb efforts.

# *Foreword*

Looking through this year's books I was particularly struck by the terrific assortment of different poems. There are the very short, the very long, serious, funny, the abstract, the philosophical and the ones that don't even look or sound like a traditional poem. But what they have all got in common is a talented young poet who has enjoyed putting pen to paper to get his or her thoughts across to the rest of us.

It is nine years since Cadbury introduced poetry into the National Exhibition of Children's Art and it has now grown into the most popular section. In fact, from this year's bumper entry level, I think it is fair to say that poetry has made something of a comeback.

As ever children speak the truth and this year's collection is no exception. It provides an illuminating reflection on life at the start of the 1990's. Certainly it will stir all sorts of emotions and perhaps bring some childhood memory of your own flooding back.

Our grateful thanks to all the teachers and parents for their help and encouragement and of course to our distinguished panel of judges who every year face the challenge of choosing the winners. I enjoyed this book very much and hope you do too.

As usual, all royalties will be donated by The National Exhibition of Children's Art to the Save The Children Fund.

Stephen Ward
Director
National Exhibition of Children's Art

# Cadbury's Ninth Book of Children's Poetry

## AWARD WINNERS – Poetry Section
44th National Exhibition of Children's Art 1991/2

### CADBURY'S CREATIVE SCHOOL OF THE YEAR AWARD
**James Allen's Girls' School**
Dulwich, London

### CADBURY'S GOLD AWARD FOR SCHOOLS
**Debenham High School**
Stowmarket, Suffolk

### CADBURY'S INDIVIDUAL GOLD MEDAL AWARD
**Catherine Wilkinson, Age 17**
Huntingdon, Cambridgeshire

### MOST PROMISING INDIVIDUAL AWARD
**Michael Davies (14)** The King's School, Canterbury, Kent
**Rachel Muers (15)** Rugby, Warwickshire

### CADBURY'S SILVER MEDAL AWARDS – POETRY SECTION

#### 7 and Under Age Group
**Anna Burgess (4)** Bewbush Home School, Crawley, Sussex
**Edward Bryant-Mole (6)** Hove, East Sussex
**Stephen Chatfield (7)** Downside School, Purley, Surrey
**Simon Cox (7)** Oldham, Greater Manchester
**Michelle De Voy (7)** Fernhill Manor Junior School, Hampshire

#### 8–11 Age Group
**Philip Gradidge (8)** Chandler Ford, Hampshire
**Rowan Taylor (8)** Whalley CE County Primary School, Whalley, Lancashire
**The children of St Patrick's School (9)** Denny, Stirlingshire
**Matthew Gill (10)** St Andrew's School, Rochester, Kent
**Tanya Darrant (11)** Woodford County High School, Woodford Green,
Essex

### 12–14 Age Group

**Lydia Garfath (12)** Newstead Wood School for Girls, Orpington, Kent
**Daniel Jones (13)** Norwich, Norfolk
**Helen Bright (14)** Torpoint, Cornwall
**Tony Roberts (14)** Debenham High School, Stowmarket, Suffolk
**Michael Davies (14)** The King's School, Canterbury, Kent

### 15–17 Age Group

**Kerry Pope (15)** Tomlinscote School, Frimley, Surrey
**Rachel Muers (15)** Rugby, Warwickshire
**Claire Wedgeworth (17)** James Allen's Girls' School, Dulwich, London
**Elizabeth Caller (16)** James Allen's Girls' School, Dulwich, London
**Tristan Carlyon (17)** John Kyrle High School, Ross-on-Wye, Herefordshire

# 44th Exhibition Tour 1991–1992

**TORQUAY – Torre Abbey**
The Kings Drive, Torquay, Devon TQ2 5JX          Tel: 0803 293593
**Friday 25th October 1991 – Thursday 21st November 1991**
Open Monday to Sunday 10.00 a.m. to 6.00 p.m.
(Last admission 5.00 p.m.)

**LONDON – Barbican Centre**
Barbican, London EC2Y 8DS          Tel: 071-638 4141 ext. 218 or 365
**Thursday 28th November 1991 – Friday 3rd January 1992**
Open Monday to Saturday 10.00 a.m. to 7.30 p.m.
Sunday 12.00 p.m. to 7.30 p.m.
Closed 24th & 25th December 1991

**HULL – Ferens Art Gallery**
Queen Victoria Square, Hull HU1 3RA          Tel: 0482 593912
**Friday 10th January 1992 – Friday 14th February 1992**
Open Monday to Saturday 10.00 a.m. to 5.00 p.m.
Sunday 1.30 p.m. to 4.30 p.m.

**WOLVERHAMPTON – Wolverhampton Art Gallery**
Lichfield Street, Wolverhampton WV1 1DU          Tel: 0902 312032
**Friday 21st February 1992 – Friday 27th March 1992**
Open Monday to Saturday 10.00 a.m. to 6.00 p.m.
Closed Sundays

**PETERBOROUGH – Peterborough Museum & Art Gallery**
Priestgate, Peterborough PE1 1LF          Tel: 0733 343329
**Friday 3rd April 1992 – Friday 8th May 1992**
Open Tuesday to Saturday 10.00 a.m. to 5.00 p.m.
Closed Sundays, Mondays and Bank Holidays

**BELFAST – Ulster Museum**
Botanic Gardens, Belfast BT9 5AB          Tel: 0232 381251
**Friday 15th May 1992 – Friday 19th June 1992**
Open Monday to Friday 10.00 a.m. to 5.00 p.m.
Saturday 1.00 p.m. to 5.00 p.m.
Sunday 2.00 p.m. to 5.00 p.m.

**PAISLEY – Paisley Museum and Art Gallery**
High Street, Paisley, Renfrewshire PA1 2BA          Tel: 041-889 3151
**Friday 26th June 1992 – Friday 31st July 1992**
Open Monday to Saturday 10.00 a.m. to 5.00 p.m.
Closed Sundays

Galleries, opening times, and tour dates subject to alteration

## CADBURY'S NATIONAL EXHIBITION
## OF CHILDREN'S ART

Organised and Sponsored by:

**Cadbury Limited
Bournville,
Birmingham.**

# First Word

## Enter: a child

That's your cue. Break a leg!
Play your part well.
Brighten up this stage of darkness;
Go and join the jesters' scene.
The audience will be your judge;
Be laughed at and mocked
But don't forget your lines.
There is no prompt,
You have had no rehearsal
And the script has not been completed.
Break a leg!

*Jane Bishop (14)*
*Debenham High School,*
*Stowmarket, Suffolk*
*(Cadbury's Gold Award for Schools)*

# I'm Looking
## ...Listening
## ...Tasting
## ...Touching,

# I'm Looking

## Through the window

I see a mesh of branches, strung up by
inexperienced knitters.
Dropped stitches, hanging threads.
Through their errors peeps the sky – wicked, blue.
They are embarrassed,
take green thread to clothe black wool.
Weave, twine, twist, ravel. Until
decency's achieved. But some
one wicked snips a thread:
they start again.

*Gabrielle Hornsby (16)*
*James Allen's Girls' School,*
*Dulwich, London*
*(Cadbury's Creative School of the Year Award)*

# The pear

It is the ear of
summer,
Glass skinned,
Crafted by the
Steady hands of spring,
It listens with its
fellows for the soft
tread of autumn.

*William Ramsey (12)*
*Aswardby,*
*Nr Spilsby, Lincolnshire*

# Autumn wind

The summer leaves know their fate.
As the wind blows through the patchwork quilt
Of copper, crimson and chestnut,
They change their jade jackets
Into crisp autumn coats,
Tailor made for autumn.

*Victoria Parkins (12)*
*Debenham High School,*
*Stowmarket, Suffolk*
*(Cadbury's Gold Award for Schools)*

# Fly

The fly is a door-to-door salesman
A quick talking,
Forceful character.
He flies like a feather
Falling on a gust of wind,
With his wings of transparent fish scales,
He's an intruder,
An unwelcome guest.
A drop of shiny oil
Spilt by a clumsy artist.
One day he'll go too far,
And the rolled up newspaper
Will arrive.
Hear him beg
As he's trapped in a corner.
Then one swoosh . . .

And a scale of wing,
Sizzles, frail on the hot bulb.

*Emma Buckingham (13)*
*Halesworth Middle School,*
*Halesworth, Suffolk*

# Madness

Throughout the Indian summer,
They were content
To mass
In that dank airless passage
Their humming home.
Its intricacies
Concealed frenetic bodies
Branded coal and crocus.

Until one chill night
They invaded the house,
Drawn to the destructive glare of the lamp
In thick velvet clusters.
Once removed
Nearly all died
Whilst frenzied survivors mated
Hoping for new life
In dying passion.

Later I faced the shining killer,
And staring
I too became light-headed
Like the wasps,
And felt their madness
At the change of season.

*Claire Wedgeworth (17)*
*James Allen's Girls' School,*
*Dulwich, London*
*(Silver Medal Award Winner)*

# Icicles

icicles are
       frozen water
       jaggy cold and slippy
       they hang on the house walls
       sharp as shears
       they glisten in the sun
       melting away

*Group Work (6)*
*Fair Isle Primary School,*
*Kircaldy, Fife*


# The moon

The moon,
Is a white see-through
balloon,
The moon is a banana,
Without any skin,
A ghost
With only a head
Completely dead,
The moon.

*Matthew Smith (7)*
*St Cedd's School,*
*Chelmsford, Essex*

# Fireworks

Screeching up high,
Fading away,
All that is left
Is petals in the sky.

*Samuel Yardley (7)*
*St Cedd's School,*
*Chelmsford, Essex*

# Toad

Pop belly,
Stuffed to the rim with air,
The sly creature,
sits like a fat conductor waiting for his trains,
The splendour of his green back,
is stained with tea.
His legs are bent,
Ready,
Ready for the high jump.
And as he peers through his sunglasses,
custard is dropped on his back,
Leaving yellow spots.
His webbed feet are
like those of a goose.
He looks
looks into nowhere,
Just waiting for his trains.

*Louise Patrick (12)*
*Halesworth Middle School,*
*Halesworth, Suffolk*

# The animal sky

The sky curves round the
earth.
Like a big fat bat.
Then it slowly glides away.

*Jenny Alderson (7)*
*Castleton Country Primary*
*School,*
*Castleton, North Yorkshire*

# Kangaroos

Live down under,
Lolloping around fields on their L-shaped legs,
Reddish-brown coat with beige beneath.
Tails like long pieces of tubing,
They bounce like Olympic high-jumpers.
When stood up it's as if they're begging,
Pouches like furry bum-bags to carry their young.

*Maxine Allen (11)*
*Ellen Wilkinson High School,*
*Manchester*

# Penguin

Big flapper
Belly tapper
Big splasher
Fish catcher
Beak snapper.

*Rebecca Clark (8)*
*Grundisburgh County Primary School,*
*Woodbridge, Suffolk*

*'Duck Taking Off'*
*Matthew Manley (6)*
*St Augustine of Canterbury School,*
*Dowend, Bristol*

# ...Listening

## ssshhh! Listen!

This bass has been walking all night,
Swinging to the rhythm,
Simply, singing.
Not off beat,
no repetition
Swaying, someone's listening.
No ending
it's still projecting
thoughts, feelings
never ending.
Brushing drums,
synchronized swirls,
comfortable as it always is as
each . . . brush . . . falls.
The piano trips over several staggering solo
semibreves,
Silence.
A subtle opening phrase.
The muted trumpet tells you,
'I guess I'll have to change my plan'
overlapping a singing note,
saxophone cuts in,
Plays a run,
plays this run again,

offering you a warm glow
that controls how you think.

You smile and close your eyes,
let me hear it one more time!

*Joe Broughton (13)*
*Chester,*
*Cheshire*

# The Blackheath Conservatoire
# of Music

Gavottes, Sonatas, Sonatinas,
Waltzes, Marches, Toccatinas.
Preludes, Polkas, Blues, Musettes,
Boogie woogies, Minuets.

Scarlatti, Mozart, Bach, Tchaikowsky,
Handel, Chopin, Kobalevsky.
Schubert, Schumann, Diabelli,
Haydn, Mendelssohn, Corelli,

Andante, Presto, Allegretto,
Dolce, Cantabile, Larghetto,
Vivace, Largo, Moderato,
Diminuendo, Non staccato.

Diminished, Dominant, Harmonic,
Major, Minor, Diatonic.
Flute, Recorder, Harp, Bassoon,
Flatter, Sharper, Out of tune.

Tinkling, Squeaking, Twanging, Pinging,
Tapping, Clapping, Strumming, Ringing.
Scraping, Wailing, Screeching, Banging,
Thumping, Bashing, Crashing, Clanging.

*Imogen Taylor (11)*
*James Allen's Girls' School,*
*Dulwich, London*
*(Cadbury's Creative School of the Year Award)*

*'Self Portrait'*
*Darren Marshall (17)*
*St Edmund Campion RC School,*
*Gateshead, Tyne & Wear*

# Fever in blue

Night-time hits the ground with a thud,
A backdrop of velvet descends,
A dark rich blue, as thick as mud,
And now the last waltz ends.

The ballroom now stands empty,
And in the still of night,
Sparks of electric blue,
Begin to pulse out bright.

The black flats of the piano,
Are played by a restless hand,
And in joins bold brash brasses,
The bass completes the band.

The romantic stars that hung in the sky,
Burst into chemical explosions,
The sulphur of these deep-set eyes,
Enhance the strong jazz potions.

The ballroom fills, once again,
Gradually numbers increasing,
But now the dancing's not so tame,
The music never ceasing.

Red-hot fiery rhythms,
Fill the raven night,
And moody blue incisions,
Ensure the cocktail's right.

Discords rebound around the room,
Bouncing off restless minds,
Spun by the beat of the music's loom,
Possessing what it finds.

Then, when the heat is too intense,
Melodies in azure arise,
The room is smothered in a moody sense,
Deepening, hazy eyes.

As the first bird sings, an amber light,
Seeps into the sky,
They'll creep away out of the night,
Until evening is nigh.

The leaden moon, sinks down low,
Weighed down by the sun,
But when the moon next silver glows,
That fever will start to run.

*Alison Everett (14)*
*Millais School,*
*Horsham, West Sussex*

# Tick tock click bang . . .

The ticks and tocks
from relentless clocks.
And a light clicking
on and a record being
played and a shout from the
street and the plodding of
feet from the hall down below.
And the creaking of
doors and the revving of
cars merge with my dreams
as I switch off my light
and become
noises in the night.

*Michael Naylor (13)*
*Queen Anne School,*
*Bootham, York*

# Can I sleep?

Next-door's feet
up the stairs
down the stairs
doors opening
doors shutting
Can I ever sleep?

My mum talking
my dad snoring
the rain pitter
pattering on the roof
Shall I go downstairs
Or try to get to sleep?

In the morning
I will be yawning
sleepy
d-o-z-e-y
So
Please be quiet.

*Emily Galvin (7)*
*Moorfield Junior School,*
*Bridlington,*
*North Humberside*

*'Untitled'*
*Oliver Heynes (10)*
*Aymestrey School*
*Worcester*

# Nodding off

Noddy's head
On my childhood clock
Past and present, an uneasy alliance.

Toytown in the middle distance
Polish as I might, the yellow brick road has tarnished
The way back goes way back no longer.

Big Ears reprimands
Wagging the minute-hand by three
But his hours are out of kilter, so who's he to talk?

Noddy's not as reliable as once he was.
He's seen better/younger days. His and mine.

After seventeen years I still can't get to sleep.

*Euan Lees (17)*
*Glasgow*

# Silence

Silence . . .
In the classroom
Chairs creaking as we settle down,
Pencils scribbling as we do our work,
Lights buzzing as the silence continues,
Feet stepping as they go to the teacher,
Voices shouting as the silence disintegrates,
Silence . . .
In our classroom?
Never!

Silence . . .
In my bedroom
The mattress squeaking as I jump on the bed,
Cupboards banging down in the kitchen,
Clocks chiming as it strikes half past,
Pipes hissing as water gushes through,
Music blaring as the silence gets drowned
Silence . . .
In my bedroom?
Never!

*Hayley Maclean (11)*
*Heath Green Middle School,*
*Horley, Surrey*

# ...Tasting

## Speaking the truth

As I,
Lie on my back
looking at the sky
I eat the snack
that I brought, on this picnic, with Andrew.

And I,
Turn on my side
To watch the sea
With its incoming tide
And ask Andrew to pass the lemonade.

So I,
Put the bottle to my lips
And take a deep breath
Before taking tentative sips
Because I'm not that thirsty and would have preferred
    Cola (anyway)

But I
Must make Andrew talk
And sort something out
Before I am caught
With Nick.

Have I
Done things as I should?
My silence is hurtful
I would speak if I could
But truth is easier to hide than let spill like acid from my
mouth.

*Elise Benton (17)*
*Salt Grammar School,*
*Shipley, West Yorkshire*

*'Self Portrait'*
*Jo Gray (17)*
*Franklin Sixth Form College,*
*Grimsby, S. Humberside*

# Strawberries

She ate strawberries with squirty whipped cream,
She licked the plate until it was clean,
She went out again and picked some more,
And ate them all again.
Stomach filled, she looked for a drink,
She found a clear bottle,
She gulped and slurped, swallowed and drunk
And turned her little tongue.
She picked herself up and staggered around,
Her eyes seemed glazed and heavy.
Suddenly, she danced about,
Now wild with delight
She ate cherries with chocolate sauce,
Once the Smirnoff had run its course,
She stood underneath the willow trees,
And caught the vein in her mouth.
She wet her hair, shook her head,
Lay down on cool wet grass
She saw all that passed under the bridge
And burned her little heart.

*Alex Black (16)*
*Trinity Catholic High School,*
*Woodford Green, Essex*

# Tasty food for Romans

Snails slither down my throat
Fattened on milk,
Roast goat.
Dormice stuffed with tasty herbs,
Delicious oysters
Swallowed whole
Bread rolls in a bowl.
Roast ham and pheasant fine,
Mulsum, honey mixed with wine.
Dainty pastries, also dates,
These are tasty from our plates.
If I lived in Roman time,
These would be
Favourite foods of mine.

*Michelle De Voy (7)*
*Fernhill Manor Junior School,*
*New Milton, Hampshire*
*(Silver Medal Award Winner)*

# ...Touching,

## Hedgehog

A hedgehog is prickly. I held a
Hedgehog yesterday. It felt funny.
      It felt funny inside.
It turned my tummy over.

*Emma Gregory (5)*
*St Catherine's School,*
*Camberley, Surrey*

## Sparrow

A bundle of feathers hits the glass,
Slides to the floor.
I move boxes and kneel,
Lift the small body in cupped hands.

Under the half-closed lids the eye is dull as stone,
A drop of blood glints like a ruby on the open beak,
Each feather is still, as if carved from marble
But the heart beats wildly against my thumb.

I hold it out in my hands like an offering
And instantly they are empty,
The bird is just a smudge against the sky.

I held an ounce of life in my hand
For a moment.
But now it is gone.

*Elizabeth Caller (16)*
*James Allen's Girls' School,*
*Dulwich, London*
*(Silver Medal Award Winner)*

# Hands

The tiny pink fist rises up;
The delicate small fingers open and close
As if grabbing the air.

The crayon moves quickly across the paper,
Fingers drop it with ease,
The hands wriggle with delight at the creation.

Sweating and tight with worry,
Bitten nails manipulate a pen;
Fingers drum across the exam paper with anxiety.

Wrists move through the air with grace,
In flashes of pattern and speed they show thoughts:
The voice needs accompaniment; worn hands suffice.

The old wrinkled fingers lie motionless.
Only a twitch sometimes stirs the dust,
They have served their time well.

*Rachel Collinson (12)*
*Peterhead, Grampian*

# And I'm Thinking.

## Jelly

Why does jelly always wobble?
I try to stop it but it just won't quit
I force it on to my spoon
And bring it closer to my mouth
I open up wide and . . .
      Plop
It's in the bowl again.

*Liam Sroka (11)*
*St Mary's RC JMI School,*
*Hornchurch, Essex*

*'Eating Bread and Honey'*
*Gemma Geddes (7)*
*Anna Ritchie Special School,*
*Peterhead, Aberdeen*

# Grown-ups!

My Dad says,
'Timothy,
TIMOTHY!
Are you listening?'
'Yes Dad . . .'
'Look at me when I'm talking to you!'
'Yes Dad.'
'How many times have I told you?'
Too many
'If I've told you once I've told you a thousand times.'
'Yes Dad.'

My Mum says,
'BORED?
In my day we were never bored.
We didn't know the meaning of the word!
We didn't have time to be bored.'
'Yes Mum . . .'
'CAN'T?
There's no such word as can't!
Young people today don't know how lucky they are!
We never dreamt of owning a car.'
'Yes Mum.'

My teacher says,
'Are you listening to me?'
'Yes Miss . . .'
'You'll never learn anything if you don't listen.'
'Yes Miss.'
'Don't answer back!'
'Yes Miss.'

I listen,
I don't speak,
But I think a lot.

*Timothy Dimon (11)*
*Allertonshire School,*
*Northallerton, North Yorkshire*

## Questioning nocturnal clichés

Night fell,
Did it hurt itself?
The moon climbed into the sky,
Does the moon have any limbs?
The stars came out,
From where?

Cars turned their lights on.
Or was it their drivers?
Cats' eyes gleamed in the dark,
Where was the rest of the animal?
Children in the back of cars fell asleep.
Where did they fall to?

The clock struck eleven.
What with?
The hands moved round,
Where were the arms?
Day broke,
Will it survive?

*Elizabeth Boakes (12)*
*Swanbourne House School,*
*Milton Keynes, Buckinghamshire*

# Royal haiku

They all say 'God save
The Queen': I don't know what
To save the Queen from.

*Daniel Burwood (12)*
*Swanbourne House School,*
*Milton Keynes, Buckinghamshire*

# Fat cat

Why is my cat so fat?
        Because he's got babies in his tummy
        Boys can't have babies.
                    I know.
But mine can.

*Aran Clyne (5)*
*Ysgol Penmorfa,*
*Prestatyn, Clwyd*

# Only trying my best

The cat brings a present for its owner
How does it know he doesn't like mouse?
'Perhaps,' thinks cat, 'I should have kept it alive for my
  owner
Then maybe he wouldn't have thrown me from the
  house.'

The cat brings a present for its owner
How does it know he doesn't like bird?
'Perhaps,' thinks cat, 'it's because of the feathers that my
  owner
Has thrown it away. Hating bird! It's never been heard.'

The cat brings nothing for its owner
How does it know why he's glad?
'Perhaps,' thinks cat, 'he's learnt to catch them himself
But if I become obsolete it will be sad.'

*Barnaby Smith (15)*
*Burnham Grammar School,*
*Slough, Buckinghamshire*

# Time

I like to make a little time
It's time to get up
It's time to wash
It's time for breakfast
And time for school
I hang my coat and beret up
It's time to read and write
and draw
It's time for milk and biscuit
bars
It's time for you to run around
It's time for lessons
Then time for lunch
More lessons; it's time to go
At home it's time for ballet class
And time to practise music
It's time for tea and then
a bath
It's time for a story and then my supper
It's time for bed
It's time to sleep
But I've not had any
TIME FOR ME.

*Laura Elder (6)*
*Belsize Park,*
*Lisburn, County Antrim*

# Seven ages of woman

As a baby, the world is blissfully without prejudice
Everyone has parent control, no one has bowel control.
Then comes the secure playgroup life of paper-plate masks,
And abstract, bright paint splashings on A4 paper,
Proudly held to the fridge
By a magnetic, alphabetic army.
The first tentative day at school, huge doors and rooms,
signs
Asking you to please wash your hands, and round the
walls
Posters of kicking k and curly c
A is for apple, B is for boat, I is for I want
I want to play in the sand tray
I want the blue crayon
I want my go
I want my mummy
Take a huge step and you're in middle school
Beginning the long, hard road that is
Adolescence.
At first, when nine and ten, boys and girls are a separate
entity
The opposite sex is not even human
We don't play with girls, they smell
So do boys – girls join in!
When leaving to go to big school, the two halves are
intimate
Involved in two-week relationships
Or not involved in anything if ugly or a 'late starter'
Upper school holds terrible rumours of caning, mountains
of homework,
Exams, bullying, torture,
Blazers

At fourteen, some look only nine years, others easily
sixteen
These are days of unfairness and hardship
For some, depression, tears, stress, crash diets and
unhappiness,
Wanting to change as fast as fashion
Caring about the environment, or pretending to,
Becoming politically aware, quoting and misquoting
The division is clear, because the others have a life
Of contentment and clear skin,
For this group, permed hair and huge hoop earrings
Worried about boyfriends and the next episode of *Home
And Away*
For the others, a green mohican, ripped Levi's and Doc
Martens,
Selling *Militant* on the street corner
A clear division, two definite groups.
But united, because at this age all everyone secretly
wants to do
Is to return to the world of half-day school,
The *Flumps*
And wishing, whilst watching *Battle Of The Planets*, that
Zoltar would win.
After the eternity of adolescence age starts to worry
many.
Even at twenty-one, feeling over the hill.
Working as a receptionist or a brain surgeon,
Teacher, bricklayer or artist,
Any one in a vast number of roles.
Perhaps marriage, maybe children, sometimes the pain of
divorce.
Then the spreading of flesh and tighter zips depress even
the most content
Grey hairs plucked out in front of the mirror

Frantic aerobics classes and keep-fit courses
Forgetting they haven't lived half their life yet.
Eventual retirement, most resigned to or happy with
their age
And looking forward to a world without a boss, or kids
to look after,
But there are those who feel frightened of what the
future holds
Insecure without family or money
Finally, nature makes a choice for each of us
Either a fading, oblivious body that the soul has
peacefully left too early,
Or a quick cutting of the life cord
Then death, a warm, deep, eternal sleep.

*Ruth Cowling (14)*
*Salt Grammar School,*
*Shipley, West Yorkshire*

*'Scarves'*
*Maxine Jackson (16)*
*Fairfield High School,*
*Droylsden, Manchester*

# Bottle

I sat staring at the opaque greenness
of the finger-pinched bottle
as the chipped wooden ball rolled around its pitted base.
I thought of when this bottle was new,
when it held strong ginger beer
that a red-faced farmer,
threads of blood vessels crocheting his cheeks,
drank in the midday sunlight
that fell like a blanket over fields
where women and children worked,
hacking at dried and cracking corn . . .
and the sound of voices rolled around
and stopped as the wooden ball
rested at the side of the
finger-pinched bottle.

*Hannah Edwards (12)*
*Halesworth Middle School*
*Halesworth, Suffolk*

*'The School Outing'*
*Stephanie Leech (6)*
*Bishop Thornton CE*
*School*
*N. Yorkshire*

# Heroes

*STUNTMAN*

A blaze of bullets,
And I fell,
Tossing and twisting
Ready for the impact,
On to a bed of dried grass
That cushioned the landing.
A 'Cut' and 'That's in the can!'
Revealed to me a pleasure
And I laughed joy
That, with dripping tears,
Made for me a soft pillow
And a full pay-cheque.

*SOLDIER*

Ablaze from bullets,
I fell
Tossed and ripped by the impact,
I twisted down
On to a bed of nailed-grass
That bit into my wounds,
Revealing to me a pain
I had never experienced.
Yet I laughed blood
That, like dripping tears,
Made for me a soft pillow
And a full sleep.

*Tony Roberts (14)*
*Debenham High School,*
*Stowmarket, Suffolk*
*(Silver Medal Award Winner)*

# Circles mean death

'Circles mean death,' said the crow from above
'Are you sure?' asked the young frog from below
'Positive,' cried the circling crow.

*Daniel Jones (13)*
*York Street,*
*Norwich, Norfolk*
*(Silver Medal Award Winner)*

# The riot

I stand, my muscles tensed
Contemplating the scene below through my binoculars.

The mob rushes, screaming below the buildings
Running swiftly through the urban maze of streets
A tidal wave of destruction crushing everything in its
    path.
The sound of the police sirens is blown away by the
    screaming of the crowd.

I grab my camera and lift it to my eye
As I depress the button I hear the shutter close.
My conscience wavers,
I am like an assassin.
I earn money from others' pain.

*David Lissauer (11)*
*St Anthony's School,*
*Hampstead, London*

# Images of terrorism

On a runway, shimmering in the desert heat,
Silently, isolated, stands the 747.
Black, hooded figures appear and disappear at the
   windows.
A hostage's trembling voice, a body flung from the plane,
An image of terrorism.

In a quiet country lane, birdsong and spring flowers,
Deserted, motionless, lies a body,
Covered now only by a black, plastic binliner,
Bullet in the head, pool of blood, hands tied.
An image of terrorism.

In the city, bustling crowds and heavy traffic
A flash, a bang, everyday life is shattered;
The car which held the bomb is now unrecognizable
Bloodstained, screaming figures scatter in all directions.
An image of terrorism.

From the warmth and comfort of a loving home,
On television, in the newspapers, every day I see
Horrifying acts of violence, disturbing and gruesome:
But, I have grown up with, and got used to seeing,
Images of terrorism.

*Linzi Sayers (14)*
*Omagh Academy,*
*Omagh, County Tyrone*

# Progress?

The men of caves
Fought with clubs
Until arrow and bow
Proved better for killing.

Huddled in fields,
Clinging to scraps
Of stinking pigskin,
The moaning men
Rubbed their chilblains.
The untrodden snow
Covered the beauty
Of the earth.

The men of houses
Fought with guns,
Huddled in trenches,
Rubbing their chilblains.
The untrodden snow
Covered the earth
They were destroying.

*Tim Connors (14)*
*Debenham High School,*
*Stowmarket, Suffolk*
*(Cadbury's Gold Award for Schools)*

# Boxes

My brother would put me in a
      SHUT-UP-JOANNE BOX
because I speak a lot.

My mum would put me in a
      TURN-ON-*NEIGHBOURS* BOX
because she likes it.

My dad would put me in a
      GO-TO-BED BOX
because he wants me to get out of his way.

My teacher would put me in
      THE WORK BOX
because I never do my work.

My friend would put me in
      THE SAME BOX AS HER
because she likes me.

*Joanne Yates (8)*
*Gallery Young Writers,*
*Rye Art Gallery,*
*Rye, East Sussex*

# We apologize for the fault in transmission

In the House of Commons today
There was
SURPRISE!
On both sides of the chamber,
When a backbench MP
No one had ever heard of,
Announced his decision
To go and take a running jump
Into the Thames.

In an emotional address
He ended a three-year run
Of completely meaningless talk.

Figures released today indicate
The trend towards complete
Public indifference continues . . .

> I need to communicate.
> Who will pull down this wall of words?
> I cannot escape my head,
> I cannot be you.
> Where is the feeling,
> The understanding I need to talk with?

. . . with lines of emotion cut,
Nothing is getting through.
Contact is impossible
And the situation looks likely to worsen.

But now for the weather . . .

*Nicholas Perks (17)*
*Dalkieth,*
*Mid Lothian*

# Computer hacker

I can control
Yet I am not the controller;
I can steal or kill;
They will never know.
I could be rich
But never famous.

I am just a shadow
In the darkness of a megabyte.
A malfunction or a power cut
Covers the light.

They know I exist;
They can feel my presence
Yet they have no power over me.
I can control their lives,
Their money, my money.
The world belongs to me.

*Douglas Gibbons (14)*
*Debenham High School,*
*Stowmarket, Suffolk*
*(Cadbury's Gold Award for Schools)*

# I'm In...
# I'm Out...
# At Home...
# At School,

# I'm In...

## Who is living next door?

The removal men come and go:
Like yo-yos their strings get entangled.
Packing cases pile themselves in acrobatic poses,
Lions jump through hoops all around them.
Bees busying about their chores,
In the compact hive next door.
A voice of thunder crashes around the echoing rooms,
The sun cringes,
And cowers behind a cloud.
A tumble of words
Spilling out,
Rippling over my ears.
A waterfall of foreign phrases,
Twisting themselves into patterns.
They mean nothing to me.
A splash of distorted English,
Then the flow stops,
Dripping only occasionally.
The removal men disperse.
The house stands silent,
Then the screen door opens,
And a cracking voice
From the record player begins to sing . . .
'Mein hit der hat drei echen . . .'

A serpent begins to slither from inside the house,
A long leg encased in khaki trousers,
And tall black wartime boots.
My new neighbour breathes in deeply,
My eyes are elastic
And stretch open to breaking point.
His eyes fall on mine,
My own snap back into shape.
My body is in the Arctic,
My mind in England.
That moustache!
Those eyes!
That hair!
It is him.
He smiles,
His front teeth are cracked,
His voice cracks the air,
'You want some candy, little girl?'
My feet jump mindlessly to attention.

*Helen Bright (14)*
*Torpoint,*
*Cornwall*
*(Silver Medal Award Winner)*

# My granny's gairden

I mind my granny's gairden
It was braw
And then she moved,
And noo she lives
In a cooncil flat
And aw she has
Is a windae box.

*Caroline Byrne (9)*
*St Patrick's School,*
*Denny, Stirlingshire*

'A Bedspread for Granny'
Sarah Johnson (17)
Franklin Sixth Form College,
Grimsby, S. Humberside

# The visitor

Each day
At Joan's
Bakey comes.
John Bacon. Bakey is his nickname
A nickname without origin
(Or so it seems, maybe a reason
Long forgotten)
He is hairless and toothless.
''ello', he says, 'any un in?'
And Joan opens the door.
She takes his coat and hat,
(A regular routine)
And hangs them in the cupboard under the stairs.
I once got my finger caught in that door.
Bakey sits in his armchair.
'What's on the telly, eh Joan?'
'Snooker.'
Snooker.
'Where is that remote control, Bakey, you sittin' on it?'
'Noo.'
'Where is it then, eh?'
Joan looks for it –
In between the cracks in the sofa,
On the window sill.
On the pink flowered carpet,
Between her set of plastic dolphins
And on the table
When she just could have switched it on.
Snooker.

Bakey either sits there, eyeballs fixed on the screen,
  moving only
to blink,
Or asleep.
Bakey is wearing this pale,
Faded, tea-stained,
Hole infested,
V-neck, slightly too small,
Green jumper that he has worn for years,
As long as I have been there.
Champ (bestest doggy in the whole wide world)
Lies on the carpet licking Joan's bare feet.
Joan is staring at the lightbulb,
Trying to work out how yesterday's *Neighbours* ended.
The lampshade is on a shelf on top of a few books;
*Kylie & Jason – Life Beyond Neighbours*
A dictionary
And the *I Love Animals Album*.
The walls have been stripped.
The stairs are bare
You can smell emulsion in the garage
A basin has been removed.
'My Brian has left me.'
The house was to be decorated a fortnight ago.
Is the Bakey
A substitute?

*Lydia Garfath (12)*
*Newstead Wood School for Girls,*
*Orpington, Kent*
*(Silver Medal Award Winner)*

# What does it matter?

'Brace Face, Brace Face,'
She looked at my teeth,
Then made a grimace.

'Four Eyes, Four Eyes,'
I turned round and shouted,
To the girl I despised.

Her face went red,
And to me she said:

'What does it matter,
If one girl is fatter?
Why should you care,
About the boy who is fair?
Why should you fret,
If you're unlike the set?
Why do the rest,
Always follow the best?
Isn't it a shame,
We have to be the same.
Why can't faces,
Have glasses and braces?

I thought for a bit,
Then made my reply,
'You called me Brace Face,
You hypocrite, why?'
'I'm sorry,' she answered,
With a guilty stare.
I said, 'That's all right,
I don't really care.'

Do you think that last line is really true?
It's not for me. Is it for you?

*Isabella McRae (13)*
*Islington, London*


# Jigsaw puzzle

I'm a puzzle, mottled and varied.
My life pieced together clumsily,
Placed together to make one colourful me.

But just as some pieces of a jigsaw
Don't arrive in the box,
Pieces of me are always missing.

I look for these pieces every day,
But how do I know what I'm searching for,
Except that it must fit the gap.

Some pieces are stamped on,
Some get torn and ragged,
Some get thrown out.

I struggle to keep my pieces together,
While others try to move my pieces around
And take my puzzle apart.

*Despina Theophanous (14)*
*James Allen's Girls' School,*
*Dulwich, London*
*(Cadbury's Creative School of the Year Award)*

# Night time

I don't like night time,
I don't like the bear in my room.
I don't like going to the toilet in
                              the dark,
But I do like a cuddle.

*Kerry Johnston (5)*
*Herne CE Primary School,*
*Herne Bay, Kent*

# There are many things

There are many things which we can fear
Spiders, dark nights, walking home
Alone.
The threat of war.
Closed spaces, open
Spaces. Death.

There are many things which we can think of
Questions, answers, memories
And the smell of toast.
Buttercups in summer fields, daisies
In a vase, the birds
Singing. Chocolate fudge.

There are many things
We only fear
Because we think.

Imagine
The fear of buttered toast,
The happy thought of darkness.

Maybe what we fear most is our thoughts.

There are many things we can think we fear
Spiders, dark chocolate, walking birds
Alone.
The threat of fudge.
Closed buttercups, open
Daisies. Death.

There are many things
We only think
Because we fear.

Imagine
The happy thought of war,
The fear of buttered memories.

Maybe what we fear most is ourselves.

*Catherine Wilkinson (17)*
*Buckden,*
*Huntingdon, Cambridgeshire*
*(Individual Gold Medal Award Winner)*

*'My Nightmare'*
*Charlotte Hull (8)*
*Daven County Primary School,*
*Congleton, Cheshire*

# The mirror man

The mirror man
Is locked out
Of our world
By a shield of glass,
Faithfully
Mimicking the world in mime.
A slave
Of fear,
Afraid of our first-hand life,
He opts instead
To become the mirror man.
There he stays,
Ensnared,
Sandwiched in glass.
He is helpless,
Caged for ever.
The mirror man
Is reliant
On others
To fulfil
Life experiences
He misses for himself.

*Nathan Connelly (13)*
*Debenham High School,*
*Stowmarket, Suffolk*
*(Cadbury's Gold Award for Schools)*

# Of our own kind

Some say
That those who are mad
Are said
To have seen the face of God.

Thus,
Their visions
Are considered holy,
And their dreams
Are honoured.

As for us,
We
Hide them away
In white-hard rooms,
Cowed,
As animals.

*Livia Ratcliffe (14)*
*James Allen's Girls' School,*
*Dulwich, London*
*(Cadbury's Creative School of the Year Award)*

# First day at church

It was a day of relaxation,
supposed to be, anyway.
Slowly we pushed open the door to the church.
Given a book, we took a seat.
I turned the fragile pages,
each page identical.
The smell was stale and the colour,
an aged yellow.
A scent of wallflowers floated on a breeze
and passed softly by.
Looking up, I found them,
standing in fresh water on the pulpit,
which took me back to my infancy
when the flowers were in full bloom
as I rolled on the fresh grass . . .
and the sun at its hottest.
A smell of candles filled the nave,
a touch of smoke and stale burning,
just like when Dad over-cooked the toast.
The vicar trotted up the aisle,
a soft squeak in his shoes,
like a baby mouse.
He spoke in a deep, crisp voice
as the sun lit the stained glass window
and a faint smell of old tobacco
drifted round and round in a loop of infinity.

*Stephen Morris (12)*
*Halesworth Middle School,*
*Halesworth, Suffolk*

# Visitors at an exhibition

The artificial air
Brushed their pearl-smooth faces
As they stood so still
Upon the moving walkway
Made from the latest material,
Laminated (P4) rubber –
Artificial,
Of course,
In the exhibition room.

Tall synthetic girders,
Supposedly steel,
Towered above
Pin-point antennae,
Protruding
From their domed helmets –
Radiation ionizers,
Of course,
In the exhibition room.

'What's that?'
The adolescent asked.
'I think it is a . . .'
A synthesized voice broke in on them:
'This is a relic from 1990 –
Over one hundred years ago.'
'What was it used for?'
'Writing, of course,'
'What's that?'
'I don't know.'

*Paul Roberts (13)*
*Debenham High School,*
*Stowmarket, Suffolk*
*(Cadbury's Gold Award for Schools)*

# I'm Out...

## The truant

Tam Broon often plunkit schule,
For lessons he couldna abide,
Up tae the Myot he'd gae,
An push aw his schule work aside.

He likit warm June best o' aw,
When the days were sae bricht and lang,
And the Carron wis bonny and blue,
An' aw the wee birds chirped an sang,

When fitstep he heard he'd hide,
In case it was Polis or Janny,
If caught he wad stammer an say,
'O please, dinna tell my Mammy.'

*Group Work (9)*
*St Patrick's School,*
*Denny, Stirlingshire*
*(Silver Medal Award Winner)*

# Osprey

Scottish,
Fisheater,
King-of-the-hills,
Wildly
– Talon tipped –
Soaring the air.

Sun spotted,
Amber eyed,
Lord-of-the-skies,
Flying into
Extinction,
Egg-thieves' favourite.

Grandly,
Helpless,
Against these men,
Drifting,
Circling,
A burning silhouette.

*Layla Beattie (12)*
*Argoed High School,*
*Mold, Clwyd*

# Fishing

Dad says 'Right, get some ragworm Amy.'
A tortured groan comes from behind him.
I open the newspaper to find wriggling, squirming,
grotesque ragworms.
I grab one of the red demons and shove it quickly
on the devilish looking hook glinting and gleaming
in the sun.
It's inside burst out – Ugh!
Thank goodness that's done!
Now for the cast.
I hear the juice dripping from the ragworm as it
throws itself about frantically trying to disgorge
itself from the lethal point.
All of a sudden I felt the urge to be spiteful
BOP – Wheeeeeeee
Over goes the fishing rod!
Over goes the bait!
Twenty minutes later I heave at the rod.
Cor that's heavy!
A clump of seaweed emerges from the marine
coloured water.
My hopes plummet
'Never mind,' says Dad, 'we'll go and have some
fish and chips from the shops.'

*Amy Scammell (10)*
*Lincewood Junior School,*
*Basildon, Essex*

# Haiku

I walked on the bank
Saw my face in the river
And wished I hadn't.

*Adam Rosenthal (13)*
*St Anthony's School,*
*Hampstead, London*

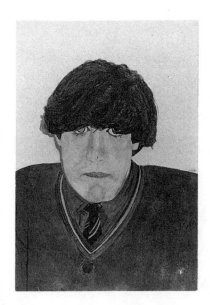

*'Ugly Duckling'*
*Chris Pattison (13)*
*St Patrick's High School,*
*Co. Armagh, N. Ireland*

## Programme cover

I slap down 50p
For an Ipswich Town programme.
I gaze at the cover
For a couple of seconds,
And to my amazement
I see my own printed face
Staring up at me
In front of the crowd.
I remember,
It was hot,
It was August,
Town v the Owls.
The roar ravaged my ears.
The first game of the season.
There, on the programme,
My brother sits upright,
Biting his fingernails
With excitement and hope.
And me?
I am looking anxious,
Apprehensive,
Knowing my team
Is going to lose.

*Evelyn Freeman (14)*
*Debenham High School,*
*Stowmarket, Suffolk*
*(Cadbury's Gold Award for Schools)*

# Go

The stampede, Phew.
Everyone trying, Phew.
To keep up, Phew.
With, Phew.
All the others, Phew.
Fifth lap, Phew.
Coming up, Phew.
My feet, Phew.
Feeling like, Phew.
Lead, Phew.
Eighth lap, Phew.
Now, Phew.
My legs, Phew.
Shouting to, Phew.
The brain, Phew.
To stop, Phew.
Last, Phew.
Lap now, Phew.
Finished,
PHEW.

*Simon Jarvis (11)*
*Whalley CE Primary School,*
*Whalley, Lancashire*

# Recipe (for a holiday)

A pound of shells.
A crab.
Stir very well.
Add some sand
with a starfish.
Beat them all.
Add a pinch of sea.
Mix quietly.
Put in a hot-dog place,
A teaspoon of seaweed.
Lay it out on a beach
In the warmth.

*Daniel Castledine (7)*
*Cloudside Junior School,*
*Sandiacre, Nottingham*

*'A Boat Trip'*
*Laura Chesman (7)*
*Hill West First School,*
*Sutton Coldfield, W. Midlands*

# The death of an Irish airman

(*A reply to* An Irish Airman Forsees His Death *by WB Yeats*)

Looking up from my plough
I saw them, quick as rabbits,
Spiralling out of a blue June sky
Twisting and rolling like swallows in flight –

There was no one else around.
I alone watched as they tumbled,
Breathing fire on one another,
Roaring and growling in anger and pain.

And then, one fell on crimson wings –
Ours or theirs, I could not tell,
And did not care as it plummeted
With predatory grace to earth.

*Tristan Carlyon (17)*
*John Kyrle High School,*
*Ross-on-Wye, Herefordshire*
*(Silver Medal Award Winner)*

# The well

The air tastes of liquorice
And smells of crushed elderberries.
The old rusty handle flakes like ash.
I wind down the rope and the bucket swings,
Startled,
Like a shot pheasant.
Then smacks on to the water and gargles till full.
I turn the handle back again
And think of a girl who bobs as she walks,
Like a floating apple.
She too heard the rope creak like a branch in the breeze.
I wake up
And pour the water in my jug.
The water sings a scale from G to E.
And then, as I walk away,
The sun melts into the western hills.

*Michelle Barnes (12)*
*Halesworth Middle School,*
*Halesworth, Suffolk*

# September song

She is trying not to notice
That the leaves are turning red
And she's singing as she's skipping,
A song that's in her head.
Too soon the sun sets pale
On the windfall's heavy gold,
While on the endless humming wires
The swallows sing their old
September song.

*Clare Robertson (15)*
*Bewdley,*
*Worcestershire*

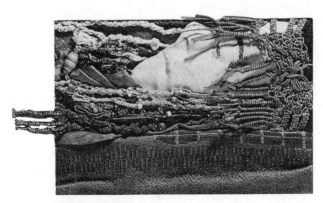

*'Eastern Delight'*
*Caroline Broome (16)*
*Franklin Sixth Form College,*
*Grimsby, S. Humberside*

# Teenage party

Hello! Come in, they're all in there.
Laura, who's your lad?
Doesn't matter, we'll smuggle him in,
Just don't tell my dad.
Turn it down! Oh, hi there Gemma.
Great, you brought some booze,
I'll take your coat, and give me that.
It's this way for the loos.
Hey Lizzie, go and talk to Tom,
He does, it's not a lie.
Look over there, he's by himself,
Go for it! Don't be shy.
Troy, don't chuck the crisps around,
They're everywhere, you louse.
You're not going anywhere
'Til you've tidied up this house.
Oh God, Mum, go upstairs,
Everything's under control.
Trust me, yeh, it's going well,
Sort of, on the whole.
What was that! Something smashed.
Nick's bleeding did you say?
Oh no, the priceless china bowl.
Nick, are you OK?
Careful with that beer, Huw,
The sheepskin rug! Stop!
Tobin, get the doorbell,
Huw, get the frigging mop.
When is it going to end?
Another hour at least.
Let's put some quieter music on,
And try to get some peace.

Who's that lying on the floor?
What? Your name is Chris?
Chris who? I wonder,
You're not on my list.
Yes Mum, I've swept the pieces up,
You look like you've been sick.
Parents here? Whose? Oh,
Has anyone seen Suzie and Nik?
Dad, there's a chauffeur at the door,
Shall I send him on his way?
He won't go without a fiver,
Give me some money and I'll pay.
Who's been sick? Where?
I just don't care anymore.
Tell the lout to clear it up
And get up from the floor.
Only five more people left
And they're all in the same car.
Oh, except for the two train-missers
Chris someone-or-other and Karl.
Dial-a-cab should be here soon,
One-thirty I think they said.
Then everyone will've gone home
And I can go to bed.

*Rosie Bray (14)*
*Lady Eleanor Holles School,*
*Hampton, Middlesex*

# Passing

My buspass is my passport;
It's just ten minutes' ride,
From Brixton into Dulwich,
It is the great divide.

No soldiers here, no checkpoints,
No great forbidding wall,
But manners, language, customs,
You have to change them all.

From Palladiums to loafers,
And Chipie to Chanel,
Karan, then into Naf Naf,
From street-cred into swell.

These kiss like Continentals
Or shake a manly hand:
These nod a casual greeting
And too much talk is banned.

'Wicked', 'safe' and 'well 'ard',
Or 'fab' and 'brill' and 'great',
'Really super, darling',
Or 'it was blindin', mate'.

I think that I'm bilingual,
I think that I can pass;
But I'm a tourist really,
And I'm travelling second class.

Would I rather be a 'Raga' or a 'Jagger'?
Would I rather be a 'Shazza' or a 'Sloane'?
I think that all this class
Is just a load of farce –
I'd really rather make it on my own.

*Lucy Pyne (14)*
*James Allen's Girls' School,*
*Dulwich, London*
*(Cadbury's Creative School of the Year Award)*

# Are feathers better than umbrellas?

Up Heatherside, rainy, cold
I waited by the bus stop.
Near to me a girl
Covered in feathers
I tried to make conversation –
'What time's the next bus?'
'How much is a return?'
She grunted
I tried
To make conversation –
'Cold, isn't it?'
She grunted
I tried
'Are feathers better than umbrellas,
Do they keep you dry?'
She grunted
I wished I'd taken an earlier bus.

*Kerry Pope (15)*
*Tomlinscote School,*
*Frimley, Surrey*
*(Silver Medal Award Winner)*

# Minutes from Waterloo

Grey concrete walls, furred with city dust, angle up
    around us,
Precise buildings, and a tangle of tagliatelle carriageways.
We stride briskly into the black socket of the underpass,
Traffic rumbling ominously overhead,
Stilletto footsteps amplified in a quick staccato rhythm.
An open circle, an oasis of sky, flanked by concrete
    tunnels.
Six teenagers with no plans for tomorrow hang around
    like wasps,
Their bright clothes wounding the exact, pale concrete;
White eyes stare like blank, blind lenses, dulled and
    glazed.
In the underpass a shanty town, folds away for the day,
A nocturnal city of plastic sheets and cardboard blankets,
Our footsteps echo, the harsh sound intimidates and
    empty eyes follow.


White boats unrolled the Thames, bright signs stole our
    money,
Voices drowned under the orchestra of car horns and
    percussive engines,
The moving beat of cosmopolitan London hurried the
    day past.

Back to the station, heavy bags colliding with tired legs,
    pace slowed.
A man begs for money – his mind struggling behind
    drugged eyes;
An old man unfolds his home, unwrapping a flute and
    empty cap;
His melancholy tune pierces through the noise of traffic,
And drags behind us like a shoelace, as we hurry
To catch the train that will get us home for supper.

*Catherine Clarke (13)*
*Parkstone Grammar School,*
*Poole, Dorset*

*'Down & Out'*
*Jacqueline Roberts (16)*
*Hatch End High School,*
*Harrow, Middlesex*

# Cement

Cement.
The big, grey blob
Is poured out like sludge
On to the brick.

The sharp, metal spatulas
Spread the mixture evenly.
It slides like a large mud pie
Into the porous brick's cavities.

Another brick is placed.
The cement is smeared
Like the jam inside a Victoria sponge.
It begins to set.

The brick is now firmly placed.
The cement has done its job.
The original sludge is now
Supporting a structure.

*Geoffrey Lloyd (12)*
*Tockington Manor School,*
*Tockington, Avon*

# At Home...

## When I lived in a flat

When I lived in a flat I was three,
and I used to pull the cat's tail!
I did it till my mum shrieked at me.
She said, 'Laura, stop pulling the cat's tail,
You'll hurt the poor thing.'
I liked pulling the cat's tail.
It was all long and cuddly.

*Claire Warder (7)*
*Carshalton, Surrey*

## Pulling

My brother
Is good at pulling.
He pulls my hair.
He pulls the curtains.
He pulls his tongue out
At all my friends.

*Natalie Hargreaves (6)*
*Whalley CE County*
*Primary School,*
*Whalley, Lancashire*

# First attempt

He crawls to the table,
Climbs up the bars of his chair
On to his bumper seat
And starts eating,
Picking up the minuscule portions
Of mashed sausage,
Peas and chips
With his new toy,
A fork.
His hand wobbles,
The peas fall,
But the sausage and chip
Still cling to the blunt prongs.
He's half an inch from his gaping mouth.
His hand jerks,
The sausage falls.
Then the chip.
But the fork goes on.
He bites the metal.
He lets out a frustrated wail.

*Iain Jaynes (12)*
*Debenham High School,*
*Stowmarket, Suffolk*
*(Cadbury's Gold Award for Schools)*

# My brother

My brother argues with baby,
and baby argues with mum,
and mum argues with dad,
and dad argues with baby,
BUT . . . my brother just smiles.

*Graham Simons (8)*
*Bedford Junior School,*
*Bootle, Merseyside*

*'Cry Baby'*
*Geraint Evans (13)*
*Moatfield Middle School,*
*Redditch, Worcester*

# My folks

Dad is the funniest,
Mum is the best,
Lucy is my helper,
and Daniel is a pest.

*Heidi Fish (7)*
*Auchenblae Primary*
*School,*
*Kincardineshire*


# My dad and his sport

My Dad watching TV,
Sit down and watch Barnsley v . . .

Near half time the score is even,
A goal scored by Owen Arch Decan.

1 – 0 to us and still trying hard,
Oh no, he's booked us with a red card.

Trying harder than before with ten players on the pitch,
Brendan O'Connell slowing down 'cos he's got a stitch.

Good tackle, and wot a pass,
Running fast, ooh bad crash.

Half time's here so get me a cuppa,
Mash it well and put in some sugar.

The match is on,
Come on, come on.

Where's me tea?
About time too, wher've you been? (Essex and back?)

Sit down and shurrup,
Go on Cooper, tek it up.

Good, he's took it quite far,
Bad luck, it hit the bar.

What a match, I'm quite glad it's dun,
But I do wish Barnsley had WON!

*Laura Baker (10)*
*RA Butler Junior School,*
*Saffron Walden, Essex*

## My dad's chair

My dad has a favourite chair
I'm not sure of the colours of it
But I'll just say 'brown' for now
It goes backwards
He rests on it when he watches television
The cat goes on it
He says 'Shoo Tabatha!'
We never get a chance
To go on it.

*Victoria Geddes (5)*
*Havannah County Primary School,*
*Congleton, Cheshire*

# Mum's on the 'phone

It's Friday night and it's dark at home,
I'm in bed and I'm scared alone,
I creep downstairs but I should have known . . .
Mum's on the 'phone.

It's Saturday morning,
I want to go out,
At first I call 'Mum,' but then I shout,
'I want to go swimming or go to the town.'
I call it again and then I frown,
I walk to the hallway, but I should have known . . .
Mum's on the 'phone.

It's Saturday evening, I'm watching TV,
The programme has finished and there's nothing to see,
I call through to Mum,
'What shall I do?'
She says, 'Hang on a minute, I'm talking to Sue.'
I go out of the lounge and I should have known . . .
Mum's on the 'phone.

It's Sunday morning, there's nothing to do,
I hear Mum's voice say, 'What about Waterloo?
Yes, you should leave at 3.00 sharp.
I'll meet you at the cafe when it's getting dark.'
I sigh, and walk slowly into the hall,
And guess who's there?
No one at all,
I go to the study and I should have known . . .
Mum's on the 'phone.

It's Monday morning but there's a day off school,
I get up, remember and shout, 'OH, COOL!'
We're going out so I shout to Mum,
She's probably in bed, the day's just begun.
Then I hear voices, chatting downstairs,
I go through to Mum's room but the bed is bare.
I go downstairs but I should have known . . .
Mum's on the 'phone.

It's Tuesday night and it's dark at home,
I'm in bed and I'm scared alone.
I creep downstairs and see Olivia . . .
Mum's off the 'phone but she's got a visitor.

*Jennifer Robinson (10)*
*Bengeo,*
*Hertfordshire*

*'Portrait'*
*Hannah Keever (11)*
*St Michael's Grammar School,*
*North Finchley, London*

# Black corduroy skirt

It was tight and restricting
And much too long
With a waist four sizes too big
And I absolutely hated it
But Mum really liked it
So I had to wear it again and again.

It was too tight at the knees
But too wide at the waist
And much too smart for me
And I couldn't get rid of it
No matter how much I hated it
I had to wear my BLACK CORDUROY SKIRT!!

*Jo Sutherland (11)*
*Welton CE School,*
*Welton, Northamptonshire*

# 'You see how easy it is'

'You see how easy it is,'
My mother said today,
'To pick up your clothes from the chair,
And hang them all away.'
But I was not being lazy and
I did not think that she'd mind.
I only left them out obviously
So they'd be easier to find.

'You see how easy it is,'
My father said last night.
'If you wipe the mud from your football boots,
And make them clean and bright.'
But I was not being dirty and
I did not leave them there for him.
I just thought when I played today,
They would get just as dirty again.

'You see how easy it is,'
My sister said this morning.
'If you return things that you borrow,
And this is your final warning.'
But I was not trying to keep them.
I could have given them back before,
I just thought it would save asking,
To borrow them again once more.

I really am not untidy,
I don't mean to be unclean,
I wouldn't keep what is not mine,
Do you understand what I mean?
'You see how easy it really is,'
I said to them all just now,
'I was only trying to save some time
Do you understand me now?'

*Matthew Gill (10)*
*St Andrew's School,*
*Rochester, Kent*
*(Silver Medal Award Winner)*

# Christmas Day

Mum put the tree up in a room
But did she remember me?
Dad put the balls on the tree
But did he remember me?
They put the tinsel on the tree
But did they remember me?
They put the lights on the tree
But did they remember me?
They put the angel on top of the tree
But did they remember me?
They opened all the presents
But did they remember me?

*Aimee Gill (7)*
*Swindon Village Primary School,*
*Cheltenham, Gloucestershire*

# Grandma

I like my grandma
Because she gives me
Strawberries and ice cream,
She always makes a cake,
And makes brandy sauce
And gives me sweets.
'Don't tell mum!'

*Jeremy Martin (7)*
*St Cedd's School,*
*Chelmsford, Essex*

# The birthday

Stacked three high,
The generations of hands
Grip the knife
That slices into the cake.

The infant,
With her hand outstretched,
Pebble-smooth and warm,
Her eyes fixed hungrily
On the cinnabar-coloured icing,
Impatiently waits
For her forthcoming feast.

Her mother's hand,
The bridge between the ages,
Contrasts with
The unadorned simplicity of the child.
Beringed fingers with painted nails
Tense, ready to listen to the stories,
Which, like creased old photographs,
Are brought out at family gatherings.

Grandmother,
Hand eroded by time,
Her eye caught by the candle shimmer
On the cake-slice,
Remembers –
A life-time ago –
A wedding gift.
Crumbs fall on to the table cloth;
She brushes them away
With a sweep of her hand.

*Caleb Bailey (14)*
*Debenham High School,*
*Stowmarket, Suffolk*
*(Cadbury's Gold Award for Schools)*

# RIP

Everybody whispers
Over the clatter and bangs
Being made by the Bhuddists
In our house  –
Praying for my grandmother,
Helping her on her way to after-life.

A picture of her hangs,
Half-smiling
On the decorated walls  –
Tassled in branches of cloth
With holy and spiritual writing,
As the Bhuddists meditate for her.

Then all the adults step forward,
Up in front of her portrait,
Lining up
Then bowing low three times,
Fragrant sticks in hands
Brought forward and put in turn in a stand
Before my grandmother.

Though it was death
I'd bear to think
It wasn't bad for her, death  –
An old-age pensioner
With dyed black hair,
A fragile woman,
Easy to break,
With naked gums like a baby's.

Every time she came to stay,
Caseloads of pills,
Ointments too . . .
Most of all
Her shining false teeth
That sank into a cup of water every night.

We were so close
Grandmother and me,
But I was relieved . . .
Don't get me wrong,
She knew herself
What had to happen.

As the thickening smoke rises
Members of the family cry –
Partly the smoke,
Or is it goodbyes?
She died happily
In a contented sleep;
Though I felt deprived –
I never got to say goodbye.

*Khoan Ly (14)*
*Ellen Wilkinson High School,*
*Manchester*

# My grandfather's war

Trapper Wild, they called him,
Seventeen.
An evacuee,
Cycling through green lanes,
Under tall trees,
Past fields full of hops,
Laughing with his new-found friends.
A peaceful year in Kent.

Trapper Wild, they called him,
Eighteen.
A raw recruit in Portsmouth,
Training hard,
Swinging on rope bridges,
Dodging thunder flashes
With his new-found friends.

Trapper Wild, they called him,
Nineteen.
God, this is it!
A Royal Marine in Scotland,
Salvaging torpedo-torn ships
That carry the echoes of screams
From friends who have gone,
Hidden in frozen waters.

*Rachel Knowland (12)*
*Debenham High School,*
*Stowmarket, Suffolk*
*(Cadbury's Gold Award for Schools)*

# Last month he died

Last month he died
From a prolonged illness
Although he didn't suffer
Of course the family gathered round
But only because . . . well . . . because he'd died.

Everyone sent flowers
Yes, I did see yours, and thanks
No of course they weren't too small
It's the thought that counts.

Yes he's buried in St Andrew's
Under that quaint old tree
You know the one with white flowers
Yes that's right, near Mrs Fry.

No, I haven't got a headstone yet
They're about £600
Oh, yes I can afford it
I just haven't had the time.

Now what was it I came for?
Oh, that's right I remember now
I wanted some flowers
No, not for the grave
Just to brighten up the house.

*Allison Judd (16)*
*Great Cornard Upper School,*
*Sudbury, Suffolk*

# Home

Do you remember that day we wandered through that
    slum that stank of squalor?
Through the shadows of high rises,
Past the 'No ball games' signs?
The graffiti shouted 'Anarchy', 'I waz ere', and 'Stu luvs
    Sharon',
A battered orange Mini parked on the yellow lines,
And a lady with a mask of wrinkles stared from between
    chintz curtains,

Glaring decisively at whatever she saw,
Somewhere a baby screamed alone,
A dog barked dementedly hungry,
A half-grown tree lay broken on the floor,
And you shivered at the sight,
Wrapped your coat around your shoulders,
Led me through the lager cans to somewhere safe and
    warm.
Now you ask me where my family lives,
And where I come from,
Wrap your coat round tighter, dear,
I'm going to take you home.

*Kate Bowgett (13)*
*Gledholt,*
*Huddersfield, West Yorkshire*

# At School,

## On my very first day at school

I got up in the morning
And s    t    r    e    t    c    h    e    d.
I padded to the bathroom
And reached,
H
I
G
H
For my toothbrush.
My clothes hung high in the cupboard.
I stood on my tip-toes
I tried to make myself a giant
To reach them.
I felt as though I was growing,

'It's time to go,' Mum said.
It seemed miles
Oh, what a way to go,
A million, trillion miles.
I said, 'Don't leave me!'
Too late.
She – – – – – – – – – – – – – was gone,

I reached H for my peg
I
G
H
I knew only the **BIGGEST** and
Strongest giant could reach it.
Oh, how heavy my coat was.

I walked into the class room.
I was shivering.
She gave us some work.
I need a pencil.
I took one from the teacher's desk.
The teacher said 'Where has my pencil gone?'
I asked if I could go and throw something away.
I took the pencil and threw it away
And hoped it would turn up another day.

The bell rang **RING RING!!**

I jumped out of my skin
My mum was waiting outside.
She said, 'Well, what was it like?'
I said, 'I can't wait till tomorrow!'

*Lucy Crisp (12)*
*St Gregory's Comprehensive School,*
*Bath, Avon*

# My teacher says

My teacher says:
we should not drop litter
My teacher says:
we should pick litter up
My teacher says:
there should be more bins in the streets

My teacher says:
we should not talk
My teacher says:
we should behave
My teacher says:
we should be quiet when she is talking

But the only thing she
has not said is 'work'
Shall we tell her?                    (Shh)

*Clare Taylor (11)*
*Scargill Junior School,*
*Rainham, Essex*

'Shadows'
Claire Davies (15)
Croesyceiliog
Comprehensive School,
Cwmbran, Gwent

# My teacher

My teacher is like a bouncy bed
Comfortable and safe but fun
Like sunrise, calm but welcome and
bright
She's a strawberry, juicy and sweet
A warm and sunny summer day
A squirrel busily scuttling around.

*Rebecca Mansell and Natasha May (9)*
*Pentlepoir County Primary School,*
*Saundersfoot, Dyfed*

# About my writing

Long long ago when I
Did my messiest writing
My teacher said, 'Beautiful'
And he wrote 'Good' in my book.
I wonder why he wrote 'Good'?
Today I did my neatest
And he said it was awful.

*Kate McWilliams (8)*
*St Ives, Cornwall*

# George, Gemma and *The Guardian*

I saw them every morning before school.
George having his breakfast,
Gemma having a snack.
Playing cards set out – games to play.
I was dropped off at eight o'clock,
Dad had to go to work.
Four miles of bendy country lanes.
Passed the lady clearing the cow muck
      from her gate.
We could be late for school if the cows
      were on the road.

      Life in the country can be strange.

Front page of *The Guardian* – there they were.
George ringing the bell for the last time,
Gemma playing tennis.

There are only nine children in the village.
The country school is about to close,
It was open for nearly three hundred years.

      Life in the country can be sad.

Now I see them every morning waiting at
      the crossroads.
Our older sisters catching their bus.
George and Gemma start a new term at a
      different school.

      Life in the country carries on . . .

*Alice Bourke (8)*
*Whitrigg,*
*Carlisle, Cumbria*

# The unknown schoolgirl

Her report card describes her disposition as
'Of gentle nature; is a hard-working girl.'
She was always well-presented, and took pride
In her appearance.

She never disagreed with her teachers
But often with her less obedient peers.
Her exercise books were always immaculately clean
Her handwriting was neat and quite readable.

In Chemistry she always took the necessary precautions
Yet still gained the correct expected and unexpected.
The correct reaction between Rock Salt and Blue Copper
    Sulphate.
In Maths her answers were concise and self-explanatory
In History she would reel off the entire story
Of the Peasants' Revolt without a single mistake
Her music marks were always high.
She played in the orchestra on three different
    instruments.

Her annual report marks were 'A' grades
Her exam marks were never less than ninety per cent
On Parents' Evening, hers were told
What an 'Intelligent, Talented and Sensible'
Daughter they had – 'Mature and Level-headed'

Her report profile was flawless, but for one heading
'Relationship with Peers'
For there was none.

*Rachel Ablett (14)*
*Newstead Wood School for Girls,*
*Orpington, Kent*

# Emma and Rebbecca

Emma and Rebbecca sit behind us,
And oh, the fuss,
'That's my pen.' 'Oh no it's mine.'
'Shut up Emma.' 'Shut up yourself.'
'What's your phone number?' 'What's yours'?
'Aint gonna tell yah.'
'Won't tell you mine, then.'
'Fine.'
'OK, let's work now.'
'OK.'
And I say, 'Shut up you pair,' and they say
'Don't tell me, tell her!'

*Kelly Bambrick (10)*
*Causeway Green Junior School,*
*Oldbury, West Midlands*


# Philip's poem

The day is like an elastic band
It stretches out longer and longer
When I'm at school.
But when the evening comes
It snaps back
Before I have time to play.

*Philip Gradidge (8)*
*Chandler Ford, Hampshire*
*(Silver Medal Award Winner)*

# Revision

Drugged by Madonna's latest album
I take a trip through Jewish history

Two decades later I turn up the volume

Two weeks
And then I will face the music

*Catherine Wilkinson (17)*
*Buckden,*
*Huntingdon, Cambridgeshire*
*(Individual Gold Medal Award Winner)*

# The cavemen

Under the stage, in an alley of mattresses and paper, we
    dwelt:
Timmy, Johnnie and I. It was dark there:
Blackboard black, black ink black, and scholar's gown
    black.
But did we take a torch? Only when we looked at
        Timmy's naughty magazines.
We were too virile to take a torch.
Only scaredy-cats took a torch.

Breaks and lunchtimes were the best times. Having our
    biscuits
There and talking about morning lessons was strangely
    enjoyable.
Sometimes people rehearsed plays when we were down in the
    'caves'.
Suddenly, I would say, 'KV', and we would lie still under
    the mattresses, not breathing if we could manage it.
We were rarely caught.

When we were nine and too old to use the I-didn't-
    know-the-rules excuse,
We went there and discovered the airing system.
Timmy's Swiss army knife loosened the gauze and we
    were in.
We kept crawling like James Bond and Steve McQueen
    in *The Great Escape*.
It was like a cave – pitch black. I led the way, my jelly
Hands in front to see if there was a wall to bump into.
The first time we stayed on the main path,
But other times we did not.

Finally, one misty, cold, boring day, when we were ten,
We went down the 'cave' and found Billy Thomson's and
    Jason Bell's signatures all over the wall.
Someone else had entered our secret place.
There was no point in going there now.
We were no longer cavemen. We were homeless.

*Michael Davies (14)*
*The King's School,*
*Canterbury, Kent*
*(Silver Medal and Most Promising Individual Award Winner)*

# Boarding school – two-generation tennis

They come in carloads, greeting part-time children
    With painted smiles; there is little love
Beneath the made-up faces,
    No chance to thrive across the physical miles.
And we, the privileged, are left
    With what their money can buy:
An education – and Sunday afternoon
    Polite conversation; glimpses of a real world.
They are the sometime parents;
    Weekends are Adopt-a-Daddy days.
They come with gifts, to sit
    Or play tennis; or the greater game
Of Happy Families.
    But the relief in the goodbyes
Is all too clear: is that guilt behind
    The stony gaze, or is it fear?
Do they realize that they have grown
    Not only alien to the goodnight kiss –
But from those they call their own?
    And when, with brief embrace
And unmet eyes, they leave us here;
    I wonder, when they turn away
If there is a conscience in that tear?

*Sarah Mulvey (16)*
*Ringmer, East Sussex*

# And I'm Laughing.

## Nativity chaos

The choir has lost a bongo drum,
Instead they're using a tin.
A baby angel tore her robes,
And Herod is on the gin.
Teacher is having a breakdown,
A king is out cold on the floor,
A Roman is having a swordfight,
And now there's a hole in the door.
The curtain goes up on time, though,
The audience gasping for breath,
For Mary is wearing a sheepskin cloak,
And Joseph is wearing her dress.
The stagehand presses a button,
And sandbag falls on to stage,
It lands on top of a choirboy,
And now he's a paper-thin page.
The teacher's gone to the funny farm,
A student is standing in,
A shepherd ate some plastic straw,
And all his teeth fell in.
The baby started crying,
And then he fell down dead,
They soon came up with an idea,
And used a cat instead.
They go to take a final bow,
The stage begins to snap,
They all fall to the basement,
But there's no one left to clap.

*Cathryn Riley (12)*
*Carlton Le Willows Comprehensive School*
*Gedling, Nottinghamshire*

# Sides

A- side, B- side, lee side, sea side
Your side my side low side high side
North side South side East side West side
Thin side wide side worst side best side
Left side right side front side rear side
This side that side off side near side
Kerb side road side light side load side
Wrong side right side dark side bright side
Top side flip side slip side grip side
Loss side gain side print side plain side
Smooth side rough side soft side tough side
Loose side tight side air side ground side
Inside outside upside DOWNSIDE

*Stephen Chatfield (7)*
*Downside School,*
*Purley, Surrey*
*(Silver Medal Award Winner)*

# Dad, I want

Dad,
      I want a hamster,
Or a gerbil
Or even a rabbit
Dad says to save
Up some pocket money.

Dad,
      I want a dog,
Or a cat
Or even a turtle
Dad says there's no
Room in the house.

Dad,
      I want a kangaroo,
Or a crocodile
Or even a koala bear
Dad says there's nowhere
To keep them.

Dad,
      I want a dolphin,
Or a whale
Or even an elephant
Dad says I can't have those
But Dad, I want a zoo.

*Gemma Webster (8)*
*Lickhill First School,*
*Stourport-on-Severn,*
*Worcestershire*

# It's a secret

I'll tell you a secret, 'Mum's' the word
That's absurd!
Shhh!

I'll tell you a secret, keep it under your hat
Why under *that*?
Shhh!

I'll tell you a secret, keep the cat in the bag
Poor thing will suffocate!

*Tanya Darrant (11)*
*Woodford County High School,*
*Woodford Green, Essex*
*(Silver Medal Award Winner)*

# The great smell of Brut

The great smell of Brut,
Is a wonderful pong,
According to Gazza,
But he's got it wrong.

The great smell of Brut,
Is a locker-room joke,
Smacks of randy pub evenings,
And swirling fag smoke.

But he splashes it on,
He struts and he poses,
While the women who watch him,
Hold on to their noses.

*Lucy Cary-Elwes (16)*
*James Allen's Girls' School,*
*Dulwich, London*
*(Cadbury's Creative School of the Year Award)*

*'Study of Male Nude'*
*Darren Marshall (17)*
*St Edmund Campion RC School*
*Gateshead, Tyne & Wear*

# Gossip

Well my second cousin
met a boy
who shook hands with
the aunt of someone
who lived next to
this person who saw a girl
once talking to this dark young boy
whom previously she had seen pass in the street
that man, y'know the one with the electric blue hair
who has been formally introduced
once at a cocktail party
in North Wales
to that bloke with the yellow Beetle
anyway this bloke with the yellow Beetle
used to work in the same co-operative house
as the bloke who was having an affair with
that woman with the . . . ummmm you know
the one whose mother looks like the Queen Mother
well anyway
I met him
God . . .
what was I saying again
Bugger
I've forgotten what I was gonna say now!

*Heather Bock (15)*
*Callington Community School,*
*Callington, Cornwall*

# She made love to Plato . . .

She made love to Plato,
She made love to Pompey,
No great man could resist her way
Or her passion.

She made love to Caesar,
And Augustus his son,
Her bright lipstick was of colour crimson
And adorned their cold mouths.

She made love to Napoleon,
Then Alexander the Great,
Seen by none, but her lovers: for t'was late
And she was quick.

She ravished Isaac Newton
And Archimedes of Greece.
'Och!' she said, 'Men of science are really quite neece!'
For she was Scottish.

Aristotle was handsome,
Cicero was sweet,
For her, each was gorgeous when she and they did meet,
And she kissed their Roman noses.

Mrs Ira McGillicuddy,
Cleaning lady at the fine arts museum,
When no one could see 'em,
Made love to the busts.

*Daniel Wicksman (16)*
*Tomlinscote School,*
*Frimley, Surrey*

# Memories

Do you remember that day?
Do you?
When you walked right into it,
Huge!
Your whole shoe was in it,
SQUISHY!
And there was no grass,
YEUCH!
But it didn't smell,
PHEW!
That ice cream
on your shoe!

*Brett Fitzcharles (10)*
*Causewayhead,*
*Stirling, Stirlingshire*

# Autumn picnic

One autumn day,
Out on a spree,
Went Willie the wasp
And Bertie the bee.

Willie took sausages,
Peaches and cake;
Bertie took melon,
Peanuts and steak.

First they played games
In and out of the wood;
Then they spread out lunch,
My! It looked good.

They sat down at once,
And what do you think?
They ate it all up,
As quick as a wink.

They took off their shoes
And laid down to rest.
Willie loosened the hooks
On his striped yellow vest.

When they woke up
It was getting quite dark.
Willie tooted his flute,
And Bert sang like a lark.

'Rum tiddle!' sang Bertie,
'That's the end of our spree.
And now we'll fly home
In time for tea!'

*Nathan Smith (9)*
*Swinton Brookfield Junior School,*
*Mexborough, South Yorkshire*

# I'm Angry
## ...Happy
### ...Hurting
#### ...Dreaming,

# I'm Angry

## Animals in me

When I am angry there is an elephant in me.
    I storm about the house,
    Slamming doors,
    Shouting at people.
There is an elephant inside me when I am angry.

When I am at school there is a mouse in me.
    I sit at the front of the class,
    Trying not to be noticed,
    And when I am asked a question I shrink away.
There is a mouse inside me when I am at school.

When I am frightened there is a spider in me.
    I run away and hide,
    I crawl under the bedclothes,
    Sweat dripping over me.
There is a spider inside when I am frightened.

There are many animals inside me,
    I've got an elephant, a mouse,
    And a spider inside me.
Sometimes I wonder if the mouse will,
    Frighten the elephant,
Then the spider will come out.

*Amy Reeves (11)*
*Bignold Middle School,*
*Norwich, Norfolk*

# Fight in the playground

WHAM!!
Right on my nose.
Fury was inside me,
Boiling up to the top.
'Hit him,'
My friends bellowed at me.
My insides churned.
My mind was like the sea,
Washing over thoughts,
That didn't matter.
I plucked up courage,
Ready to hit him back.
I took a small step forward,
Then another,
I raised my left arm,
He backed away,
The coward.
Whoosh.
I had missed,
Had he ducked?
Try again,
Dong. Dong.
There's the bell,
I'll get you back next play,
No fear!!

*Victoria Marshall (11)*
*Yatton VC Junior School,*
*Bristol, Avon*

# The vital ingredients for a war

Gather together blood and sand
Use creaming method, mix by hand,
Place in a pan the water and oil,
And then very carefully bring to the boil.
Whisk in chemicals
And more blood
And then maybe for flavour, throw in a Scud.
Mash up the missiles,
Garnish with pain,
Be careful when stirring
The blood tends to stain.
Grate up the corpses
Let the sun make them fry
And pick some young pilots
Fresh from the sky,
Chop up the pointlessness
Blend in the hate,
Bake in the desert sun,
Serve on a plate
And just for decoration
On the top pour
The person who started this terrible war.

*Jane Hammill (12)*
*Fleetwood High School,*
*Fleetwood, Lancashire*

# Entreaty

*(For the women of Kuwait who refused to allow their relatives to fight against Iraq. November 1990)*

Not in my name, brother, not in my name.
She is a heroine who sends her brothers there
to fight and die, but I will never be one.
She will call me coward, she who never flinches
to see them going, but if you kill in my name
you kill the one who bears it.
Take not my honour to the battle ground
to bring back stained with blood, I will deny it.
I will deny it and accept the shame,
rather than bear, until my death, one death.
Even if that death be yours, I have chosen, brother.
I will desert you, and I will die alone.

My brother, if your ghost can cross the sea,
whisper reproaches to me while I sleep,
tell of your killing and your death for me,
I feel the tears, I know how I shall weep;
but then, when you are past all praise or blame,
I will answer – No, brother. Not in my name.

*Rachel Muers (15)*
*Rugby, Warwickshire*
*(Silver Medal and Most Promising Individual Award Winner)*

# Disaster report

The reporter stands
Amidst the sightless, gazing,
Amplifying the sounds
Of dying hordes.
They are too feeble
To walk
Or even speak.
The only thankful creature
Is the fly,
Waiting,
Waiting.

Creased faces stare blankly
At the reporter.
The colour control illuminates him;
The volume is high
So even the deafest of ears
Might hear of the waste of life.
'If only,'
They chorus,
'It could happen to us,
But painlessly.'

*Keith Jaynes (14)*
*Debenham High School,*
*Stowmarket, Suffolk*
*(Cadbury's Gold Award for Schools)*

# Romanian orphans

Overcrowded, in bleak rooms,
Dirty, in unmattressed cots,
Lie silent children without a future.

*Catherine McKeary (11)*
*Coleraine High School,*
*Coleraine, County Londonderry*

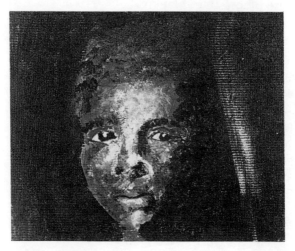

*'Portrait of a Papua New Guinean'*
*Gemma Lyus (13)*
*Honiton, Devon*

# Travelling circus elephant

The young elephant
fought the chains,
bashed the tin box
she knew as home.
Wildly she kicked
and screamed
in a frantic frenzy.
Her metal abode
enclosed her,
her chains digging
into her tender ankles,
the pain causing her
to ram her head
against the enemy wall.
Her eyes were fiery,
terrified, she mangled
her prison.
The sharp edges
of the torn metal
ripped her, cut her.
Her flanks were encrusted
in deep red blood.
Pain was written all over
her furrowed brow.

I am ashamed to be human.

*Sophie Rickard (11)*
*Whalley CE County Primary School,*
*Whalley, Lancashire*

# Golden drummers

Shut in a crate
Half bald
A turkey sits dejected.
Her brood of puny chicks
Squabble.
She remembers how
One asked her
'What is the sun, Mama?'
She had not answered.
She had not known.

*Alexandra McRae (10)*
*Canonbury,*
*London*


# At the zoo

I saw a big elephant.
It was looking for something
he couldn't find . . .
. . . his home in Africa.

*Eric Sutton (6)*
*Whalley CE County Primary*
*School,*
*Whalley, Lancashire*

# Whale

I am the giant in the tears of the sea,
Endangered,
Wasted by your fearsome harpoons.
Soon I may be gone,
And be but a large shadow,
A dark ghost,
Haunting the dream oceans
In the memory of man.

*Dylan Lally (13)*
*Ellen Wilkinson High School,*
*Manchester*

*'Welsh Black Cow'*
*Mark Tarry (7)*
*Maesbury School*
*Oswestry, Shropshire*

# I love animals

'I love animals,' the woman said,
As she put on her huge fur coat.
'I love animals' the woman said,
As she ate a juicy steak.
'I love animals,' the woman said,
As she put on her leather shoes.
'I love animals,' the woman said,
As she applied her make-up.
'I love animals,' the woman said,
'I love animals dead!'

*Joanna Rigg (13)*
*Rishworth School,*
*Calderdale, West Yorkshire*

*'The Cooling Tower'*
*David Cowburn (11)*
*St George's County Junior*
*School,*
*Shrewsbury, Shropshire*

# Under the leaves

No one sees the danger,
Not man, nor child, nor dog.
What harm could there be
In a pile of leaves?
But, below the beauty, is the beast,
Silver teeth as sharp as glass
Are sitting,
Waiting,
Hoping for food.
Not long now,
Any second,
SNAP!
It's closed,
Like a dungeon door,
On a helpless fox.
The teeth hold fast
And so does the pain.
The trap hungrily waits
For the fox to die.
Not long now!
It's getting weaker,
Weaker.
Its young stand by,
Watching,
Wishing;
Wide-eyed, they look
At the piled red leaves.

*Hannah Chenery (14)*
*Debenham High School,*
*Stowmarket, Suffolk*
*(Cadbury's Gold Award for Schools)*

# Mr Antman

Incy wincy teensy weensy creepy-crawly Antman
        Steps into a burning spot of light.
For a moment, he feels nothing,
Then runs, panicking, for his tiny, black life
As he feels the concentrated point
        Microwaving him.

When he flees, I disable him by singeing his thorax
        And then frazzle his minute, kicking legs
And watch the squirming joints vapourize, one by one,
Into an almost invisible column of smoke
Which tickles my nose
With the smell of incense  –
        Hallowing his sacrifice.

When he stops writhing and contorting
        I prod him to prolong my sadistic pleasure.
But he only crackles and pops, as his abdomen
Explodes my delusion,
Flashing in the glass,
The glass that distorts my reflection.
        And now I burn,
Flustered and cringeing with guilt.

*Miles Edlmann (15)*
*The King's School,*
*Canterbury, Kent*

# Whit a load o' rubbish

When I gawk around, it maks me mad,
Tae see a' the rubbish, it's like a pit.
Folk ir ayewis flingin' stuff awa',
When somehing guid can be done wi' it.

Ev'ry day the rubbish van comes,
An' loads o' rubbish gits chucked intae it.
But ye'll never see me doein' a thing like that,
We keep it in the shed, that's whar it's pit.

We're gonnae yase it a' again,
We're gonnae recycle the rubbish.
A' the food we dinnae eat,
Goes straight intae the dug's dish.

We also yase oor bottles again,
An' fill them up wi' ither juice'
We yase fruit peelin's fur gairdin muck,
An' auld T-shirts fur cleanin' the hoose.

Auld Christmas cairds mak guid labels,
An' I aye collect the stamp aff a letter.
Am' hopin' yez will dae the same,
A hope yez will,
YE' BETTER

*Stuart Marshall (11)*
*Fair Isle Primary School,*
*Kircaldy, Fife*

# The place where I live

The world is such a pretty place,
With everything in its proper place,
If we did not spoil it so,
More things would last and grow,
It's the place where I live, you see,
You have no right to spoil it for me.

*Richard Cager (7)*
*West Hove Junior School,*
*Hove, Sussex*

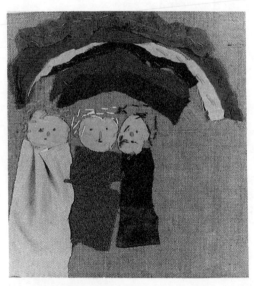

*'God with Mr and Mrs Noah*
*Nichola Cockburn (6)*
*Green Top First School*
*Doncaster, S. Yorkshire*

# I love my belt

Plastic belt
Elastic belt
Stretch – stretch – stretch
FANTASTIC belt.

*Jasmine Lehal (5)*
*Bedford, Bedfordshire*


# My box model

Now what I did is . . .
I didn't know that I could
Make this do something.
This flapping bit . . .
I didn't know that I could use
All this sticky stuff.
That flicks into here
And then it goes down into a bucket.
I pretend somebody's being poorly
And the model is a nurse's machine
I didn't know I could do this.
I bet my mum will love it.

*Paul Morris (5)*
*Havannah County Primary School,*
*Congleton, Cheshire*

# My wobbly tooth

In the middle, in the front
My tooth wobbles.
Frontwards and backwards.
It's white, my tongue plays with it.
It's nearly out,
It doesn't hurt.
My wobbly tooth.

*Kayleigh Nagle (5)*
*Lodge Hill Infant School,*
*Caerleon, Gwent*

# My glasses

I wear glasses
Because my eyes turn in.
If I didn't wear them
I couldn't see.
I like my glasses
Because they are very handy
For looking out of.
They have a very clever design
And they are a special shape.
My glasses are split into two.
The bottom is for reading.
The top is for looking.
Sometimes I don't like my glasses
Because when I go swimming
The girls laugh at me.
That's because I look different
With my glasses off.

*Edward Bryant-Mole (6)*
*Hove, East Sussex*
*(Silver Medal Award Winner)*

# Almost extinct

There is a zoo
At the end of the universe.
A creature with flesh,
Two eyes and some hair
Sits on its own.
'What is it?' they ask.
'It is a human;
The only one left;
The rest are dead,
Along with their world.
They fought each other
And killed all the animals.
They strangled the corn
With nooses of roundabouts,
Playgrounds for cars.
Space meals were eaten.
They all fell ill.'
There is a zoo
At the end of the universe
Where the last human sits
Looking at space.

*Jonathan Hart (13)*
*Debenham High School,*
*Stowmarket, Suffolk*
*(Cadbury's Gold Award for Schools)*

# ...Happy

## Mummie's skirt

Pick me up in your wonderful skirt,
all the day long!

*Anna Burgess (4)*
*Bewbush Home School,*
*Crawley, Sussex*
*(Silver Medal Award Winner)*

*'Happiness*
*(A A Milne)'*
*Kelly Moorhouse (5)*
*St Catherine's Junior*
*School,*
*Guildford, Surrey*

# Yesterday, today, tomorrow

When Mrs Cook was Headteacher
It felt black and misty
She wouldn't believe me
Angry, upset and frightened
Holding the tears in
Better than letting them trickle down.

Today – greeny blue like the pond
I stroke my guinea pig
She butts at my hand
Squeaking, like the screeching of a wheel
Pipsqueak's babies are as big as the handlebar on my bike
Sausages in a frying pan.

Tomorrow – I'll go swimming with Dad
I will do breaststroke under all the people
Tomorrow will be a dazzling, orange sun
An eye-catching red flower.

*Simon Cox (7)*
*Delph,*
*Oldham, Greater Manchester*
*(Silver Medal Award Winner)*

# Our new arrivals

Snoozing, snuffling, twitching, dreaming,
Our five black puppies
Sleep.

Yawning, stretching, grunting, rolling,
Our five black puppies
Wake.

Jumping, squealing, running, gumming,
Our five black puppies
Play.

Sniffing, sucking, lapping, spilling,
Our five black puppies
Eat.

Snoozing, snuffling, twitching, dreaming
Our five black puppies
Sleep.

*Oliver Hilton-Johnson (9)*
*Swanbourne House School,*
*Milton Keynes, Buckinghamshire*

# Public opinion

We met in nineteen forty nine,
And I still get a shiver down my spine
Every time he holds my hand.
Being in love is really grand.

He works on the London Stock Exchange.
The first gift he gave me was the 'Filofax' range.
I love his eyes and his brand new car.
Being in love is super, ya.

I met my fella on an aeroplane,
When we was coming back from Spain.
He works in Wimpy on Peckham High Street.
Being in love is really neat.

He has the most perfect face I've seen,
His teeth are white, his hair is clean,
And even though we're still at school,
Being in love is mega-cool.

We met at a rally for saving the whale,
We both got arrested and put into jail.
Last Christmas he bought me a white kaftan.
Being in love is way out, man.

We live in the same block of council flats,
We met when he helped me get rid of the rats.
He's got some money, but not a lot,
So being in love is all we've got.

*Sarah Cohen (14)*
*Ealing, London*

# ...Hurting

## I was crying

I was crying
I could not draw a circle.
I was crying
Because I could not understand.
I used compasses.
Other people knew,
But I couldn't get them to work.
I do not ask the right questions.
Who can I ask?
My parents and my teacher.
I ask them and they explain.
I still cannot draw a circle
I cried,
I could not understand,
but I tried.

*Laura Potts (8)*
*Benton Park Primary School,*
*Newcastle-upon-Tyne*

# When I am alone

When I am alone I am sad.
I feel angry inside.
When I am alone, nobody wants me.
I hide away from the playground.
I wish a friend would appear
That I could chat to.
I feel upset, I watch others.
My tears come; I put my head
Down so nobody can see.

*Michael Tao (7)*
*Buxlow Prep School,*
*Wembley, Middlesex*

*'Schizophrenia'*
*Dario Carnera (16)*
*Chadwell Heath High School,*
*Romford, Essex*

# Stutter

People laughing at me
Tears subsiding
Hesitating
Can't get the words out
The laughter is ringing in my ears
Tears running down my cheeks
I finish the story with great dididifficulty.

*Gary Stiefel (11)*
*St Anthony's School,*
*Hampstead, London*

# My parents argue

By the window
I watch some children on the lawn.
Press my cheeks against the cold glass.
See tears run down it.
Listen;
Screaming behind the door.
They slam each other's heads against the
wall with insults.
Tear hopelessly at the hair-fine thread
which attaches them both.
By the window
I smear the wet glass with my finger.
And distorted through it
I watch some children on the lawn.

*Karen Heath (17)*
*Epsom, Surrey*

# The door to sadness

I am the door to sadness,
I am the door to murder.
Open me and you will see
the blood-stained walls crying
in agony
while the murder of
two young and innocent
children took place behind me.
Ah, but it is too late for
they are dead.
I wish someone would
turn the lock
And bury my key in a
bottomless pit so I could
forget all that had
happened.

*Jamie Selway (9)*
*Lauriston School,*
*London*

*'Chimneys'*
*Group Work (13)*
*Wakeman School,*
*Shrewsbury, Shropshire*

# In my house nobody notices

In my house nobody notices,
The little holes in the bath,
The missing biscuits in the pack,
The untold jokes from last year's crackers,
Nobody notices me.

*Ruth Ireland (11)*
*St Anne's CE Middle School,*
*Bewdley, Worcestershire*


# There's something in my tum, Mum

Mum, there's something in my
                                tum.
Mum, I'm not dumb dumb.
It's like a pet that has never
                            been fed.
Now I'm going all red.
I need to go to go to bed.
There must be something in my
                                tum.
I don't like it please get it out,
                            Mum.

*Lianne Dalmon (7)*
*West Hove Junior School,*
*Hove, East Sussex*

# Asthma attack

The ground rushed towards me,
With a high-pitched scream.
Like a steam train,
Screeching at a sudden halt.

My chest heaved uncontrollably,
Sweat blurred my eyes,
Everything . . . turned a misty-grey.
I gasped for air,
Like a stricken
             man
                gulping
                    water.

I rasped a feeble 'Help!'
It sounded like a broken, hoarse croak,
I was wet with sweat,
And exhaustion – rolling
                as if in a
                  wrestler's
                    ring.

I clutched my chest,
Trying to rip out the pain,
That was tormenting my lungs.
A black cloud tore at my chest,
Trying to escape.
I was crying now,
Hot, stinging tears,
Poured ceaselessly,
Meandering down.
My wheezing,
A feverish energy,

Took hold of me,
As I pulled at the razor blade
Piercing my throat.
A black hole
        in my mind
                sucked
                    me
                        in.


I was dimly aware of the nozzle,
Thrust into my mouth,
I inhaled the medicine, slowly,
        coughing,
        choking.
My eyes cleared.
I saw the worried face of a matron,
Peering at my white face.
The sweat still came,
I felt drained of energy – but
Propped myself on my elbow,
                        smile!
                    little
                a
            managed
        I even


*William Somerville (12)*
*Tockington Manor School,*
*Tockington, Avon*

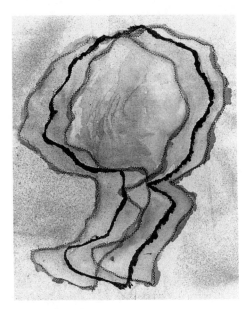

*'A Jagged Rock'*
*Holly Jones (6)*
*Corvedale School,*
*Nr. Craven Arms, Shropshire*

# The orthodontist

The orthodontist says, 'Come in,'
In I go then.
'SIT DOWN,
LAY BACK,
OPEN YOUR MOUTH.'
Then in he goes,
More like a little man mending a bridge.

Metal blocks,
Silver wire,
Plastic fillers,
I feel like a building site,
       a railway track,
       a train burning up,
When he tightens the wire.
Then out he pops with tweezers in hand.
He says, 'How does that feel?'
I relax my mouth,
I can feel the wire,
       the metal blocks,
Pulling on my teeth.
Pain throbs through my nerves.
I pretend to bite.
I clench my fists, it hurts,
I imagine sweet things,
But a picture of a building site keeps reappearing.
With men hammering,
And banging,
On ladders and scaffolding.
I think of chocolates and boiled sweets.
And the damage to my teeth,
And of my brace,
And of a building site,
And what my friends will say.

*Tiffany Frankland (13)*
*Oakdene School,*
*Beaconsfield, Buckinghamshire*

# Listen to me

What's happened?

Why is it dark? Dark, cold and silent?

Let there be sound! Let there be warmth! Let there be light!

Why is it dark?

Why can't I see, hear, feel or smell anything?

The world must have been destroyed,

I must be floating in an empty void!

What was that click?

Argh! That light, it's so bright!

It's the sun, it has to be, it's alight again.

What can I see at its heart?

I can't focus on it.

Ah! Now I can make it out!

'TESCO 60W 240V      Coiled Coil      Made in UK'

What?

The world, it's back!

It wasn't destroyed, it . . . just . . . disappeared for a while.

Thank God.

Oh! Hello.

Fine, thank you.

Who are you?

What's that beeping?

Ah! That's the machine it's coming from. What's it for?

Who's she?

Nurse?

Doctor?

What are you doing here?

Where am I?

Hey, don't leave doctor.

Why are you tucking me into this bed, I can do it perfectly well myself.

What am I doing in bed?

Don't go. What's happening?

Why are you ignoring me?

I hate being alone!

Hello, who are you?

Son?

Mum! Mum and Dad! Am I glad to see you!

Thanks, they smell lovely.

Sorry, I'm a bit tired. You don't mind if I rest a little do you?

Huh? Where'd you go. Damn, I must have drifted off. The first time they visited me and I didn't even say goodbye.

Oh! Hello doctor! How are you?

Could I have a look at that clipboard?

Give it to me!

Uh! Doctor, why can't I move my arm?

Why can't I move anything?

Answer me, damn you!

God! That beeping gets on my nerves!

Nurse! Can you explain to me why can't I move?

You say my parents are here? Great!

Hi Mum, hi Dad. Can you tell them to explain what's happening?

Mum? Dad?

You're sorry about what, Doctor?

I'll never leave what state?

What crash?

It didn't destroy my mind!

I'm fine. Listen to me. LISTEN TO ME!

*Matthew Seaborn (16)*
*Great Cornard Upper School,*
*Sudbury, Suffolk*

# Bonemarrow poem

Getting up early
Not fair, not fair,
'No food for you dear'
Not fair, not fair.
Driving off to hospital
In the dark,
Parking at the hospital
In the car park.

Going for my thumb prick
But *THAT* doesn't hurt
Going to the waiting room
Playing with the toys.
Going for a check up
'How are you doing?'
She looks down my ears
And down my throat.

Then I go for my bonemarrow.
The anaesthetist
Gives me an injection
That puts me to sleep.
Then I'm in another room
In a bed.
NOW FOR MY BREAKFAST!

Bombing to the canteen
Getting all I want . . .
Two packs of sandwiches,
Sweets and crisps.
My back's still hurting
'Mum, will you carry me?'
Jump in the car
And drive off home.

*John-Mark Piper (7)*
*Millom, Cumbria*

## The moon

The moon out
There.
The sun out
There.
The world out
There.
The whole galaxy out
There
and me stuck in my
bedroom.

*Ki Ellwood-Friery (8)*
*Bognor Regis,*
*West Sussex*

# Child and dove

*(Response to a painting by Picasso)*

Mary-Ann
please stop crying
The dove was old
he deserved a rest.
I tried to tell you
really I did,
but I couldn't.
Why?
It wasn't the right time.
Bring the ball here
we are going home.
You'll get your Sunday best
dirty.

I am praying for my dove
alone.

*Linsey Richards (9)*
*Cloudside Junior School,*
*Sandiacre, Nottinghamshire*


# Abandoned

My squashy chair, where did it go?
And where's my bed – I demand to know
Why, all my belongings have been taken away.
Where are my toys? I miss my play.
What will I do, I'm so confused,
Where's my new dish? It's hardly been used.
My scratching post and ping-pong ball,
Surely I've not lost them all.

I've turned all dizzy, I'll have to rest,
I honestly think that would be best.
But there's nothing to sit on, not even a chair,
I believe the entire house is bare.
Not a blanket can I find,
Surely I have not gone blind.
A wash may help to ease my nerves,
But I'm still panicked, it's so absurd.

Of course I'm sad, I miss all my things,
But worst of all, and a tear this brings,
I fear my owner has deserted me.
If this is freedom, I hate being free.
I long for a hand, a human touch,
I miss my master so very much.
I must eat soon, or I'll die of starvation,
But a mouse is not much of an invitation.

Sadly I understand and begin to realize,
I've been abandoned and left to die.
How will I cope, all on my own?
I wish I didn't feel so alone.
Out into the wild I slowly go,
My tail has never hung so low.
Please, someone, rescue me,

I'VE BEEN ABANDONED – can't you see?

*Claire Bancroft (11)*
*Stanton-by-Dale,*
*Derbyshire*

# Just a pawn in your hands

Like the silent flight of a hunter,
Like a silencer on a gun,
Your bullets still cut into my flesh,
Like the penetrating rays of the sun.

Like the coin with two unknown faces,
Like a dice with too many sides,
Your actions still affect my life now,
Like the rabbit that forever hides.

Like the disbelieving adult,
Like listeners ignoring the dumb,
Your turned back still leaves me here,
Like the death that turns you numb.

Like a stone that changes the current,
Like a fence that cages you in,
Your gates of pride still lock me out,
Is my love for you such a sin?

If it isn't then stop playing a game,
That involves putting me down all the time,
If it isn't then stop and think for a while,
Burn the rules and you'll be mine.

*Susan Northover (17)*
*Southfield School for Girls,*
*Kettering, Northamptonshire*

# Saturday night at Shaftesbury Avenue

The twenty-second of September
Ninteen hundred and ninety
Was a day I shall . . .
Forget.
I shall forget the brown polo-neck,
The milkshake, the ambience of that
claustrophobic bar.
I shall forget thin fingers, snooker cues
and your smile.
The slot machine and Cinzano and ice.
I shall forget the puddles lying,
Still and sensual on the pavement,
The way you splashed and threw
Your head back.
I shall forget,
Forget the way you brushed her hand,
As my throat grows tighter,
I shall forget.

*Elizabeth Wells (16)*
*James Allen's Girls' School,*
*Dulwich, London*
*(Cadbury's Creative School of the Year Award)*

# 1914

Every day we would walk down the long, winding road
And make our way towards the pub,
There we would drink our earthy bitter
And give ourselves moustaches with the frothy head.
We tried to be men, to prove ourselves.
We would laugh with the flirting girls
And nudge and wink.
But there was one whom I would never laugh at,
She had my respect, she had my heart
And every time she caught my eye or I caught hers
I would smile and blush
But I wouldn't talk,
I couldn't, for fear of making a fool of myself.
But my burning passion for her
Fired a flame
That blazed throughout my whole body.
I would rehearse conversations with her
And I could feel the velvet texture
Of her olive skin,
The sensual softness of her lips,
The seduction and agony in those deep brown eyes.

One day, my seventeenth birthday
We had a chance to prove ourselves.
War.
Once again down at the pub
We talked as heroes,
Of medals, of honour, of chivalry.
We were loud and raucous.
We sang songs of war, victory, gallantry,
And vowed to sign up.
We impressed the girls with our talk of war
And the olive-skinned girl

Looked at me proudly from under her eyes
Which fuelled my arrogance and enthusiasm.
But I was the youngest
And I cursed my parents
When they forbade me to sign up.
I wished my friends good luck
And called after them
'I will see you next year!'
And they laughed and waved.

Days rolled into months
And I would sit alone in the pub
With letters and reports
Learning of the horrors of the war,
The wasting of lives,
The shovelling of men over the top
Into a graveyard
Marked with headstones of mines and barbed wire.
I became wary and sick of war
I did not want to sign up,
I did not want to kill,
To be killed.
I wanted to stay at home
To be safe.

My eighteenth birthday came,
I was expected to sign up
But I put it off,
I didn't want to go to war, to die,
To leave the security of the village.
The girls didn't talk to me any more.
When they passed
They would hang their heads
And look at me sadly, disapprovingly.
I still longed after the olive-skinned girl
And it was always the steel sorrow in her eyes
That shamed me.

One day
Down that long winding road
She separated from her crowd of friends
And slowly walked towards me
Her eyes fixed on mine,
Her friends silently looked on.
And then,
Standing in front of me
She brought something from her pocket,
My eyes left hers and looked towards her hands,
In her long fingers she held a white feather
Which she pressed into my sweating hands,
And then walked away
To join her friends who gave me one last look
Before walking on
Walking to my funeral march
Leaving my body frozen,
My eyes hovering on the feather
As tears fell on to it
Matting the fine spines.

Men were killed in the trenches at the fronts.
But I was killed at home,
Not by a mortar shell or a bullet
But by one white feather.

*Samantha West (16)*
*Tonbridge School for Girls,*
*Tonbridge, Kent*

# Instances of you

If you were my teddy
I would pull you to pieces
But regret it afterwards.

If you were a book
I would read you hungrily
Then rip out all your pages.

If you were a spider
I would pick off all your legs
Then make you a bed of cotton wool.

If you were a belt
I would fasten you so tight around me
That I should gasp for breath.

If you were a record
I would listen endlessly to your strains
Until I was sick of the sound.

If you were a bed
I would snuggle up inside you
And then be tormented by nightmares.

If you were a car
I would drive you so fast
That I should lose control.

But you are none of these,
You are a person
And I miss you.

*Joanna Pecover (17)*
*Burnham Grammar School,*
*Burnham, Buckinghamshire*

# ...Dreaming,

## The bird who wore shoes

The bird who wore shoes was mad.
He was laughed at by everyone.
He didn't mind that at all.
He couldn't fly because
The soles of his shoes were lead.
And he couldn't swim because
He would sink to the bottom of the sea.
He couldn't do much at all.
So one day
He took his shoes off, and
He swum and flew and walked
Properly for once.

*Matthew Brown (10)*
*Park School,*
*Dartington, Devon*

# Realisation

I can recognize now where I travel –
Along dusty roads at high noon,
Where the goat tracks
Lead impossibly up vertical hills
To an azure sky.

Through this shadowed, sinister forest
Where forbidding leaves absorb
Brightest sunshine,
And shy creatures harmoniously sing
A strange refrain . . .

So I wander vaguely on again,
By midnight hills; beneath three moons;
Where a golden beast
Asks riddles of the setting sun
And declares no truth.

I can recognize now where I travel –
This forest can contain no trees
Unless in dreams,
Whilst a spirit-glow undying lights
The hills, the dusty road.

*Corinne Berg (15)*
*Newstead Wood School for Girls,*
*Orpington, Kent*

# Chaotic cliffs

The bird flew high, cutting the air,
      over the crumbling cliffs.
The waves tripped and tumbled and
      saltily sizzled.
As it flew its test, in the rarest
sky of blue boldness.

It climbed higher and higher until out
                of sight, then
At an instant, it appeared in confused flight,
Sear-soaring, stumbling and skipping.

It dived like a spitfire, out of control
And crashed against the chaotic cliffs,
And splintered and smashed into metallic bits.
Springs, coils, a scientist's kit
Sprinkled and tinkled into a fishless sea.

*Clair Chadwick (17)*
*Salt Grammar School,*
*Shipley, West Yorkshire*

# What the wolf knows

I'll hide under the covers
and wait.
She should have a surprise.
The key is under the stone
like always.
She should be here.
She should have her bright red cloak on,
so I should know who she is.
Her beautiful golden hair will flow.
She will scream.
I will eat her until
only her bones are left.
I will throw them on the fire
until they burn to a cinder.
She won't cry.
I will eat her quicker than
a lion eats a mouse.
I can see it now.
Her blood flowing like a stream.
My nose will smell her flesh.
My eyes gleam until she has gone.
I sleep like a baby.
My shining mouth glows and drips.
I know her death.

*Rowan Taylor (8)*
*Whalley CE County Primary School,*
*Whalley, Lancashire*
*(Silver Medal Award Winner)*

# Killer carrots

They arose from the earth,
Tall and thin,
They had no eyes,
Yet I could feel their cold stare upon me.
They had no mouths
Yet I could hear their voices ringing in my ears.
In armies of 20, 30, 40,
They troop into towns and cities,
People are screaming.
And shouting for help
But the carrots storm on and on.
No one can stop them as they go marching on.
All over the land,
All over the sea,
The whole world's in their power,
Soon we shall be
Slaves kneeling at their roots.

*Abigail Troop (11)*
*Friends' School,*
*Saffron Walden, Essex*

# The magic bubble

I blow a big bubble
and there I throw my two
sisters
Who moan.
I blow as hard as I can
And they drift and twirl in
the transparent bubble.
Suddenly it bursts
Like a raindrop
And my sisters fall into
the sea.

*James Grant (7)*
*Marston Green Infant School,*
*Marston Green, Birmingham*

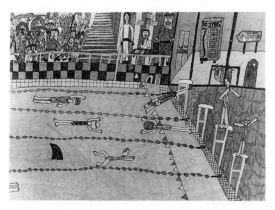

*'The Swimming Race'*
*Gabrielle Godwin (10)*
*Blue Coat School*
*Edgbaston, Birmingham*

# Wanted: a witches' cat

Wanted: a witches' cat
Must be able to jump off trees at least
And smell good things to go in my spells
It must have lovely glistening eyes to see in the dark
Must be able to fight little beast
Then we can have them for a feast
Must be strong and able to hold ten bricks
Must be magic and fly and learn all my spells from books of
hundreds years old
Balance well on my broomstick
Expert on finding mice
Knit warm socks to wear at winter
Salary a nice warm home with a cupboard of food
Apply to Meg the witch
Frog 798-9828
15 Spook Street

*Laura Mullineux (8)*
*Moorside Primary School,*
*Swinton, Manchester*


# The malicious witch

The angled shape of the malicious witch
Tattered and foul, eyes of pitch.
Her hair is spiked and her eyes are beady
With wizened skin, sardonic, greedy,
Eerie!

She has an abominable taste for magic,
Vulgar fangs stained black as ink.
A fraying broomstick with target clear,
Menacing all who venture near in
Fear!

She is blasphemous and cruel,
Shrieks malevolently like a ghoul.
Her cauldron ready, charmed with spell,
Her soul, friendless, can only dwell in
Hell!

*Donny Waisanen (10)*
*Lomond School,*
*Helensburgh, Strathclyde*

# Secret room
# (or Tutankhamun's Tomb)

Into a secret room
Little horses
Lords that guard
Wooden wheels
Gold that shone
A sealed door
Tutankhamun, may we come in?

*Hannah Moody (7)*
*Rushcombe First School,*
*Wimborne, Dorset*

*'Japanese Person'*
*Louise McGlennon (16)*
*Holyrood Secondary School*
*Glasgow*

## The unthinkable

The razor-sharp, steel bows
cut swathes through icy black,
fathomless waters.
A jagged shape appears,
outlined upon the horizon.

Inside, in the warm Salon,
men are smoking dark brown
Havanas, talking business,
or gambling away profits.
Some in evening dress, escort
elegant ladies in flowing Parisian
gowns; smiling, curtseying laughing,
bowing
as they join swirling dancers.
The orchestra playing merry
Strauss melodies from Vienna.
Down in third class many
emigrants are excitedly
looking forward to the new
life in the New World.
The Irish soon have them
all singing and dancing.
For many it would become
a dance of Death.
'Icebergs ahead,' cries the
startled, frozen Watch.
The call came too late.
Even after the shudder
ran the length of the ship,
there was no real panic –
the passengers all Knew
that the Titanic was unsinkable.

*Ashley Edwards (10)*
*Cullompton,*
*Devon*

# Cleopatra

I bracelet myself for your arrival;
Tiger eye,
Turquoise, gold wire,
All warm gently on my loaded wrists,
The heat of my woman's body.
Today I sit indoors, out of the sun.
My thoughts are a loop,
With you the beginning and end,
A panorama of our story-so-far
Like the temple walls, the stark flat friezes.
Three years have I sat here,
Reading letters from Rome.
I am tensed, coiled
Like this bracelet
I have found myself twisting
Unconsciously, the wire digging my fingers.
I hear horses' hooves, run to the window
Peer out – and quietly swear.
It is you – Antonius,
And I have noticed
The new crop of greying hair.

*Avril Huston (15)*
*Chelmsford County High School,*
*Chelmsford, Essex*

# And I'm glad, glad, glad to be me.

## Holes

I have holes in my head.
I have two holes for looking.
I have two holes for sneezing.
Earholes are for listening.
And one big hole
For eating, drinking and shouting.

*Howard Jenkins (4)*
*Whalley CE County Primary School,*
*Whalley, Lancashire*

## Salty sea

Salty sandcastle,
Salty sea,
Salty footprints,
Salty me.

*Carl Saville (5)*
*Beehive Lane*
*Primary School,*
*Chelmsford, Essex*

# My self

My mum says my nails are
disgusting.
But I like them.

My friends say I've got big ears
But they're good at listening.

I *have* got small feet
But they're good at football.

I'm right pleased with my
self.

*Toby Nightingale (8)*
*Castleton County Primary School,*
*Castleton, North Yorkshire*

'Football Fans'
Nigel Brooke (14)
Salesian School,
Longhope, Gloucestershire

# Farewell to summer

Goodbye, farewell to summer,
To hours of fun and play.
Goodbye to the red hot sun,
Which tanned me as I lay.
Goodbye to the sound of the sea,
I used to hear each day.
Goodbye to the long, light evenings,
And to the sandy bay.

Hello to the shorter evenings,
Of wind and cold and rain.
Hello to the trees stripped bare,
Oak, ash and plane.
Hello to the autumn colours,
The leaves fall in the lane.
Hello to the winter fire,
And winter tales again.

Hello to Jack Frost and to Sir Ice,
Who are now already here.
Hello to the wind so wild,
To the mist and fog so near.
Goodbye to the beach,
To the sea, so blue and clear.
Goodbye to the summer season,
I'll see you again next year.

*Lucy Daffarn (11)*
*St Andrew's School,*
*Rochester, Kent*

# The rebel child

Most days when I
Go off to school
I'm perfectly contented
To follow the rule.

Enjoy my history,
My music, my sums,
Feel a little sorry
When hometime comes.

But on blowabout mornings
When clouds are wild
And the weather in a tumult –
I'm a rebel child.

I sit quite calmly
My face at rest,
Seem quite peaceable,
Behave my best;

But deep inside me
I'm wild as a cloud
Glad the sky is thrown about
Glad the storm's loud.

And when school's over
And I'm out at last
I'll laugh in the rain
Hold my face to the blast.

*Mark Murphy (10)*
*St Helen's Junior School,*
*Brentwood, Essex*

# Adrenaline

Power surges through you
An electric shock pricks you with excitement.
Adrenaline is creeping up
A Blossom of power
It flies through you, swiftly, like a swallow
It's alive –
Like electricity
Like fire.

Lead it, direct it,
Twist and curve, hurl it
Don't let it over-rule you.
Take hold of it
Channel it with courage.

*Samantha Holden (10)*
*St Catherine's School,*
*Camberley, Surrey*

*'Starting'*
*Catherine Jenkins*
*(15)*
*Croesyceiliog*
*Comprehensive School,*
*Cwmbran, Gwent*

# Last Word

## My poem

I carry a poem
a ball in my head, it goes round
and round, backwards and forwards
till I kick it out of my head
because I have written it down.

*Lucy Orr (6)*
*St Catherine's School,*
*Camberley, Surrey*

# The 1992 Poetry Competition

The Books of Children's Poetry contain about 160 selected entries from children of all ages and are illustrated with work from the National Exhibition of Children's Art.

If you would like to enter the 1992 competition whether in the Art, Design or Poetry sections, you can write to this address for an entry form:

National Exhibition of Children's Art
Granby
Altrincham
Cheshire
WA14 5SZ

*(Please enclose a stamped/addressed envelope)*

Remember—you not only have a chance to feature in the *Tenth Book of Children's Poetry* but also to win a substantial prize.

# Index of titles

189

# Index of authors